Calculator
CONNECTIONS®

Teaching with Basic Four-Function
Overhead & Student Calculators

William B. Duffie
Telkia K. Rutherford
Alfred J. Schectman

Written by: William B. Duffie, Telkia K. Rutherford, Alfred J. Schectman
Edited by: Marcy Gilbert and Jessica Smuksta
Cover designed by: David Metzger
Interior designed by: David Metzger and Katie Bailey
Illustrated by: David Metzger

© Learning Resources, Inc., Vernon Hills, Illinois (USA)
  Learning Resources Ltd., King's Lynn, Norfolk (U.K.)

ISBN: 1-56911-974-0

Printed in China.

Contents

Introduction

Anyone can pick up a calculator and plug in some numbers, but there is a great need to understand and be able to use the calculator efficiently.

Your Calc-u-vue® calculator and this book will help explain and teach the uses of the calculator. Pages titled Teaching Notes contain instruction, examples, and activities for you to use with your students. The other pages may be reproduced as worksheets for student use.

Before you begin formal instruction with calculators, allow some time for students to explore. This will allow your students to become somewhat familiar with the general layout of their calculators. It will also eliminate distractions you may encounter by students playing with calculators while you are instructing.

In the first 38 pages of this book, you and your students will work through the various keys and features of your calculators. Students should follow each process and work along as you demonstrate on the overhead projector. Starting with page 39, specific objectives are addressed. Along with explanations of the objectives, you will find activity pages and games. Select from these activities to suit the mathematical knowledge of your students.

Meet Your Overhead and Basic Calc-u-vue® Calculators

The teacher's transparent overhead Calc-u-vue® and student's hand-held Calc-u-vue® have identical keyboard layouts and easy-to-read eight-digit displays.

Teacher's Overhead Calculator

Precisely demonstrate single and multi-step calculations and explore different problem-solving strategies. Your whole class can now easily participate in a step-by-step learning process.

Basic Calc-u-vue® Overhead Calculator
LER 0050

Matching Student Calculators

Color-coded plastic keys help all students quickly learn the operations, memory, and constant functions. And, the activity pages in this book are designed to motivate students as they learn.

Basic Calc-u-vue® Calculator
LER 0058

Meet Your Calc-u-vue® Calculator

The teacher's transparent overhead Calc-u-vue® and student's hand-held Calc-u-vue® have identical keyboard layouts and easy-to-read eight-digit displays.

The change sign key changes a number from a positive to a negative and vice versa.

Use this key to find the square root of a number.

Use this key to turn on the calculator or to clear all pending operations. It does not clear the memory.

Use the percent key with one or more of the basic operation keys.

Pressed once, this key clears the last entry only. Pressed twice, it clears all pending operations. It does not clear the memory.

This key subtracts numbers directly from the memory. It also adds negative numbers to the memory.

These are basic arithmetic operation keys.

This key stores numbers in the memory and adds directly to the memory.

When pressed once, this key brings to the display any number stored in the memory. When pressed twice, it wipes the memory clear.

This represents a decimal point.

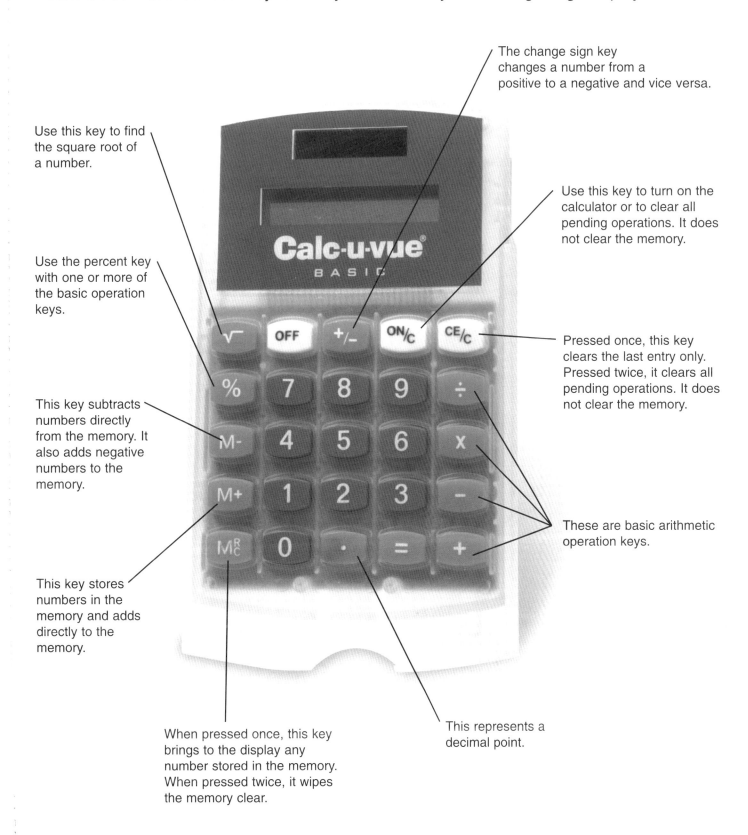

Teaching Notes

How Does Your Calc-u-vue® Calculator Work?

As you demonstrate with your overhead calculator, have the students follow along. Press the ⌷ON/C key. What appears on the display? [Answer: The number 0.]

Tell the students that it is important to press the ⌷ON/C key before starting any new problem. This will make sure that all previous information is cleared from the calculator. To avoid cluttering the instructions for key sequences with the ⌷ON/C key, we will assume that ⌷ON/C has been pressed before each problem or exercise.

Ask students to press ⌷8 as many times as they like. What is the greatest number of 8s that appear on the display? [Answer: Eight] What is the largest whole number that can be displayed? [Answer: 99,999,999]

Place your finger over the solar cells. Did the display disappear? Ask students what makes the calculator work? [Answer: Light] You might have students experiment to see how much light is needed.

Have students try all four operations by doing these examples along with you. Use smaller numbers and just addition and subtraction with younger students.

Addition: 15 ⌷+ 5 ⌷=   [Answer: 20]
Subtraction: 15 ⌷− 5 ⌷=   [Answer: 10]
Multiplication: 15 ⌷× 5 ⌷=   [Answer: 75]
Division: 15 ⌷÷ 5 ⌷=   [Answer: 3]

The student worksheets on pages 5-8 provide students practice in using the basic operations with numerical problems and problem solving.

Name _____ Date _____

Basic Addition

Press $\boxed{\text{ON/C}}$.

Press 1.

Then press $\boxed{+}$.

Press 2.

Press $\boxed{=}$.

Write what you see. _____

1. 1 $\boxed{+}$ 4 $\boxed{=}$ _____

2. 2 $\boxed{+}$ 2 $\boxed{=}$ _____

3. 6 $\boxed{+}$ 3 $\boxed{=}$ _____

4. 3 $\boxed{+}$ 2 $\boxed{=}$ _____

5. 1 $\boxed{+}$ 1 $\boxed{=}$ _____

6. 5 $\boxed{+}$ 2 $\boxed{=}$ _____

7. 4 $\boxed{+}$ 4 $\boxed{=}$ _____

8. 1 $\boxed{+}$ 6 $\boxed{=}$ _____

9. 2 $\boxed{+}$ 3 $\boxed{=}$ _____

10. 3 $\boxed{+}$ 4 $\boxed{=}$ _____

Basic Subtraction

Press ⬜.

Press 5.

Then press ⬜.

Press 4.

Press ⬜.

Write what you see. _____

1. 3 ⬜ 1 ⬜ _____

2. 6 ⬜ 2 ⬜ _____

3. 5 ⬜ 4 ⬜ _____

4. 4 ⬜ 4 ⬜ _____

5. 9 ⬜ 8 ⬜ _____

6. 7 ⬜ 2 ⬜ _____

7. 8 ⬜ 5 ⬜ _____

8. 4 ⬜ 2 ⬜ _____

9. 10 ⬜ 6 ⬜ _____

10. 3 ⬜ 0 ⬜ _____

Basically Simple

Press ON/C.

Press:

15 ☐+☐ 3 ☐=☐ __18__ addition

15 ☐−☐ 3 ☐=☐ __12__ subtraction

15 ☐x☐ 3 ☐=☐ __45__ multiplication

15 ☐÷☐ 3 ☐=☐ __5__ division

1. 100 ☐+☐ 5 ☐=☐ _____

2. 100 ☐−☐ 5 ☐=☐ _____

3. 100 ☐x☐ 5 ☐=☐ _____

4. 100 ☐÷☐ 5 ☐=☐ _____

5. 17 ☐+☐ 4 ☐=☐ _____

6. 68 ☐−☐ 17 ☐=☐ _____

7. 17 ☐x☐ 4 ☐=☐ _____

8. 68 ☐÷☐ 17 ☐=☐ _____

9. 14 ☐+☐ 6 ☐=☐ _____

10. 84 ☐÷☐ 6 ☐=☐ _____

11. 6 ☐x☐ 14 ☐=☐ _____

12. 14 ☐−☐ 6 ☐=☐ _____

13. 84 ☐÷☐ 14 ☐=☐ _____

14. 84 ☐−☐ 14 ☐=☐ _____

15. 84 ☐+☐ 6 ☐=☐ _____

16. 42 ☐x☐ 2 ☐=☐ _____

Who Says Simple?

The Acme Construction Company is building a skyscraper on land that Peter passes on his way to and from the school each day. One morning, the construction engineer came to the school to talk to Peter's class about the job. While he was there, the engineer presented these problems to the class. After carefully thinking about each problem, use your calculator to help you arrive at the correct answer.

1. The building would use about 200,000 pounds of steel, 600,000 pounds of concrete, and 2,000 pounds of glass. If 1 ton (T) = 2,000 pounds (lbs.), about how many tons did these raw materials for the building weigh? _____

2. Each of the twenty-two floors in the building would have 14,960 square feet of office space except the first floor, which has only 9,758 square feet of office space. How many square feet of this space would there be in the entire building? _____

3. The building would be about 352 feet tall. If all the floors are the same distance from each other, about how high is each floor? _____

4. The engineer said the new building would be about as tall as 8 of Peter's schools stacked on top of each other. About how tall is Peter's school? _____

Teaching Notes

Clearing Entries

As you demonstrate with your overhead calculator, have students follow along. Enter 3 [+] 4. What do we do if we want to change the 4 to a 5 without starting over?

Press [CE/C] once. Ask what number appears on display. [Answer: 3] Now enter a 5 and then [=]. Point out that pressing [CE/C] and then a 5 changes the last entry to 5. Then, pressing [=] gives 8 as the answer to 3 + 5.

Here is another example.

7 [×] 8	[Display: 8]
[CE/C]	[Display: 7]
10	[Display: 10]
[=]	[Answer: 70]

Beware: Pressing [CE/C] twice will clear all previous entries. Pressing it just once clears only the last entry.

There are other ways to clear all previous entries. Have students enter 7 [×] 4 [=]. Then press [ON/C]. What appears on the display? [Answer: The number 0]. Pressing [CE/C] once also clears all previous entries.

The student worksheet on page 10 provides students practice in clearing entries. Remind them to press the [ON/C] key only once.

Name _____ Date _____

OOPS!

We made a mistake. Change the last entry without disturbing the previous entries.

For example, if you wanted to add 3 $\boxed{+}$ 5 but accidentally pressed 3 $\boxed{+}$ 4, you could correct your mistake by pressing 3 $\boxed{+}$ 4 $\boxed{\frac{ON}{C}}$ 5 $\boxed{=}$ ____8____ .

In each of the following problems, we made a mistake on the final entry. Change the last number entered to the number in the parentheses without disturbing the other entries.

1. 5 $\boxed{+}$ 6 (8) $\boxed{=}$ _____

2. 18 $\boxed{-}$ 5 (7) $\boxed{=}$ _____

3. 9 $\boxed{\times}$ 5 (2) $\boxed{=}$ _____

4. 35 $\boxed{+}$ 10 $\boxed{-}$ 15 (20) $\boxed{=}$ _____

5. 55 $\boxed{-}$ 30 $\boxed{+}$ 10 (8) $\boxed{=}$ _____

10

Teaching Notes

Using the Memory Keys

When you turn on the calculator, 0 is in the memory. The M+ key adds the number on the display to the memory. The M- key subtracts the number on the display.

Pressing M℞c once recalls the number in memory to the display. (The number remains in memory.) Pressing M℞c twice clears the memory.

Without using the memory keys, solve (2 + 4) x (8 − 5).
In step 3, point out that students must remember the 6 from Step 1.

Step 1:	2 + 4 =	[Answer: 6]
Step 2:	8 − 5 =	[Answer: 3]
Step 3:	3 x 6 =	[Answer: 18]

Now use the memory keys to solve (2 + 4) x (8 − 5).

Step 1:	2 + 4 = M+	[Display: 6]
Step 2:	8 − 5 =	[Display: 3]
Step 3:	x M℞c =	[Answer: 18]

Solve (9 x 3) − (16 ÷ 2).

Step 1:	9 x 3 = M+	[Display: 27]
Step 2:	16 ÷ 2 = M- M℞c	[Answer: 19]

Solve (7 x 5) − (6 x 2) + (45 ÷ 9).

Step 1:	7 x 5 = M+	[Display: 35]
Step 2:	6 x 2 = M-	[Display: 12]
Step 3:	45 ÷ 9 = M+ M℞c	[Answer: 28]

The student worksheets on pages 10 and 11 provide students practice in using the memory keys.

Name _____ Date _____

Forget-Me-Nots

Use the memory keys M+, M-, and M̲C̲
to solve this problem.

(9 x 3) − (16 ÷ 2) = _____

Press ON/C.

Press 9 ⓧ 3 M+ 16 ÷ 2 M- M̲C̲.
_____19_____

Solve these problems using M+, M-, and M̲C̲. Remember to press ON/C before
each problem.

1. (12 x 5) − (48 ÷ 8) = _____

2. (100 + 60) − (8 x 5) = _____

3. (3 x 5) + (20 ÷ 4) − (80 ÷ 4) = _____

4. (4 x 9) − (7 x 2) + (28 ÷ 4) = _____

5. (42 − 4) + (5 x 3) − (54 ÷ 9) = _____

6. (36 ÷ 9) + (6 x 4) − (49 ÷ 7) = _____

7. (100 ÷ 5) − (8 x 2) + (60 ÷ 6) = _____

8. (50 − 10) + (45 ÷ 9) − (6 x 3) = _____

12

Name _____ Date _____

Don't Forget!

Use the memory keys M+ and MℝC to solve this problem.

(7 + 2) x (10 − 6) = _____

Press ON/C.

Press 7 + 2 M+ 10 − 6 x MℝC = .
_____36_____

Solve these problems using M+ and MℝC. Remember to press ON/C before each problem.

1. (8 − 5) x (7 + 13) = _____

2. (36 ÷ 4) x (13 − 6) = _____

3. (16 + 4) + (9 x 8) = _____

4. (55 − 30) + (50 ÷ 2) = _____

5. (17- 9) + (81 ÷ 3) = _____

6. (84 ÷ 6) x (54 ÷ 18) = _____

7. (27 ÷ 9 + 8) + (5 x 8 − 12) = _____

8. (32 ÷ 8 − 3) x (6 x 7 − 2) = _____

9. (16 ÷ 4 + 3) x (72 ÷ 9 + 1) = _____

13

Teaching Notes

Using the Addition Constant

As you demonstrate with your overhead calculator, have students follow along. Enter 2 [+] 2 [=] [=] [=] [=] and so on. What seems to be happening? [Answer: 2 is being added to the number in the display each time you press [=].] Is there a way to tell which 2 is the constant being added? [Answer: No]

Now try this: Enter 1 [+] 2 [=] [=] [=] [=] and so on. What seems to be happening now? [Answer: 2 is being added each time.]

Point out that the second number (addend) in an addition problem becomes a constant when [=] is pressed repeatedly. That is, each time the [=] key is pressed, the second addend is added to the current number on the display.

2 [+] 5 [=]	[Display: 7]
[=]	[Display: 12]
[=]	[Display: 22]
6 [=]	[Display: 11]
8 [=]	[Display: 13]

The student worksheets on pages 15 and 16 provide students practice in using the addition constant.

Name _____ Date _____

Adding Over and Over

Use the addition constant to solve the following problems.

5 $+$ $-$? $=$? $=$? $=$?

Press $\boxed{\frac{ON}{C}}$.

Press 5 $+$ $=$ 5 $=$ 10 $=$
15 $=$ 20

Use the addition constant to solve these problems.

Press the $=$ four times. Record your answers.

1. 3 $+$ $=$ ___ $=$ ___ $=$ ___ $=$ ___

2. 7 $+$ $=$ ___ $=$ ___ $=$ ___ $=$ ___

3. 10 $+$ 5 $=$ ___ $=$ ___ $=$ ___ $=$ _

4. 50 $+$ 25 $=$ ___ $=$ ___ $=$ ___ $=$ ___

5. 8 $+$ 2 $=$ ___ $=$ ___ $=$ ___ $=$ ___

6. 10 $+$ 3 $=$ ___ $=$ ___ $=$ ___ $=$ ___

15

Adding Constantly

Use the addition constant to add 8 to each of these numbers:

16, 32, 29, 100.

Press $\boxed{^{ON}_{/C}}$.

Press 16 $\boxed{+}$ 8 $\boxed{=}$ __24__ $\boxed{=}$ __32__ $\boxed{=}$

__40__ 29 $\boxed{=}$ __37__ 100 $\boxed{=}$ __108__

1. Using the addition constant, add 3 to each of the following.

  4   29   56   152   97

_____ _____ _____ _____ _____

2. Again, using the addition constant, add 15 to each of the following.

  30   100   305   15   6

_____ _____ _____ _____ _____

A billing clerk in a mail-order company wanted to determine the total charges for the out-of-town orders. In addition to the cost of the items ordered, the clerk must add a shipping and handling charge of $2.10 to each order. Use the constant function on your calculator to figure the total charges for the following orders.

3. $18.90 = _____

5. $123.45 = _____

4. $5.29 = _____

6. $99.49 = _____

16

Teaching Notes

Using the Subtraction Constant

As you demonstrate with your overhead calculator, have students follow along. Enter 20 $-$ 2 $=$ $=$ $=$ $=$ and so on. What seems to be happening? [Answer: 2 is being subtracted from the number in the display each time you press $=$.]

The second number (subtrahend) in a subtraction problem becomes a constant when $=$ is pressed repeatedly. That is, each time the $=$ key is pressed, the subtrahend is subtracted from the current number on the display.

50 $-$ 5 $=$	[Display: 45]
$=$	[Display: 40]
$=$	[Display: 35]
$=$	[Display: 30]

Once a constant is set, entering any number followed by the $=$ key will subtract the constant from the entered number. In this example, 5 is the constant.

50 $-$ 5 $=$	[Display: 45]
6 $=$	[Display: 1]
8 $=$	[Display: 3]

The student worksheets on pages 18 and 19 provide students practice in using the subtraction constant.

Subtraction Over and Over and...

Use the subtraction constant to solve: 18 [−] 3 [=] [=] [=] [=]

Press [ON/C].

Press 18 [−] 3 [=] <u>15</u> [=] <u>12</u> [=] <u>9</u> [=] <u>6</u>

Use the subtraction constant. Press the [=] four times and record your answers.

1. 24 [−] 4 [=] ___ [=] ___ [=] ___ [=] ___

1. 90 [−] 10 [=] ___ [=] ___ [=] ___ [=] ___

2. 200 [−] 25 [=] ___ [=] ___ [=] ___ [=] ___

3. 81 [−] 9 [=] ___ [=] ___ [=] ___ [=] ___

4. 55 [−] 5 [=] ___ [=] ___ [=] ___ [=] ___

Subtracting Constantly

Use the constant function to subtract 5 from each of the following numbers:
35   27   9   100

Press ⬚%ᴄ.
Press 35 ⬚- 5 ⬚= _30_ 27 ⬚= _22_ 9 ⬚= _4_ 100 ⬚= _95_

1. Using the subtraction constant, subtract 10 from each of the following numbers.

     49   87   174   402   11

_____   _____   _____   _____   _____

2. Again, using the subtraction constant, subtract 8 from each of the following numbers.

     24   13   57   163   8

_____   _____   _____   _____   _____

3. A bank teller made a big mistake and added $6.50 to several accounts. After identifying all the accounts where the mistake occurred, the teller must now subtract $6.50 from each of the following accounts and record the new correct balances. Use the subtraction constant on your calculator to find the new totals.

   $18.67 $51.79 $146.29 $16.20 $142.08

_____   _____   _____   _____   _____

Using the Multiplication Constant

As you demonstrate with your overhead calculator, have students follow along. Enter 2 $\boxed{+}$ 2 $\boxed{=}$ $\boxed{=}$ $\boxed{=}$ $\boxed{=}$ and so on. What seems to be happening? [Answer: The number in the display is being multiplied by 2 each time you press $\boxed{=}$]. Is there any way to tell which 2 is the constant multiplier? [Answer: No]

Try entering this: 2 $\boxed{x}$ 3 $\boxed{=}$ $\boxed{=}$ $\boxed{=}$ $\boxed{=}$ and so on. What seems to be happening now? [Answer: The display is being multiplied by 2 each time.]

Point out that the first number (factor) in a multiplication problem becomes a constant when $\boxed{=}$ is pressed repeatedly. That is, each time the $\boxed{=}$ key is pressed, the first factor is multiplied by the current number on the display.

Once a constant factor is set, entering any number followed by the $\boxed{=}$ key will multiply the entered number by the constant. In this example, 5 is the constant.

5 $\boxed{x}$ 3 $\boxed{=}$		[Display: 15]
$\boxed{=}$		[Display: 75]
$\boxed{=}$		[Display: 375]
$\boxed{=}$		[Display: 1875]
6 $\boxed{=}$		[Display: 30]
8 $\boxed{=}$		[Display: 40]

The student worksheets on pages 21 and 22 provide students practice in using the multiplication constant.

Multiplying Constantly

Use the multiplication constant to solve the following problems. Press the = three times to arrive at the correct answer.

2 x = = =

Press ON/C.

2 x = __4__ = __8__ = __16__

Solve the following problems using the multiplication constant. Record your answers. Press the = three times for each problem.

1. 5 x = _____ = _____ = _____

2. 60 x = _____ = _____ = _____

3. 3 x = _____ = _____ = _____

4. 10 x = _____ = _____ = _____

5. 50 x = _____ = _____ = _____

6. 20 x = _____ = _____ = _____

Teaching Notes

Using the Square Root Key

As you demonstrate with your overhead calculator, have the students follow along. Enter 25 $\sqrt{}$. What answer is on the display? [Answer: 5] Did you need to press $=$ to get the answer? [Answer: No]

25 actually has two square roots, +5 and –5. That is, $\sqrt{25}$ equals +5 because 5 x 5 = 25. Also, $\sqrt{25}$ = –5 because –5 x –5 = 25. The calculator only displays the positive square root.

Here are more examples.

1. $\sqrt{49}$ [Answer: 7]

2. $\sqrt{225}$ [Answer: 15]

3. $\sqrt{2.25}$ [Answer: 1.5]

4. $\sqrt{5}$ [Answer: 2.2360679]

5. $\sqrt{0.01}$ [Answer: 0.1]

6. $\sqrt{0.0004}$ [Answer: 0.02]

The student worksheet on page 29 provides students practice in using the square root key.

Call Me a Square (Root, that is.)

Write a key sequence that will find the square root of a given number.

Example: $\sqrt{81}$

Key sequence ⬜ 81 √

Answer ___9___

Find the square root of the following. Write a key sequence to show your work and record your answer on the space provided.

1. Square root of 16   2. Square root of 144   3. Square root of 64

_____   _____   _____

4. $\sqrt{625}$ 5. $\sqrt{58}$ 6. $\sqrt{6561}$ 7. $\sqrt{120}$

_____   _____   _____   _____

8. Square root of 16.16   9. Square root of 25.49

_____   _____

Teaching Notes

Using the Percent Key

The ⟦%⟧ key on your calculator may be used with each of the four operation keys ⟦+⟧, ⟦−⟧, ⟦x⟧, ⟦÷⟧. This permits us to solve four basic kinds of percent problems very easily.

As you demonstrate with your overhead calculator, have students follow along.

1. **Adding a Percent to a Number**
   An item is priced at $35.00. If the sales tax is 8%, what is the total cost of the item?

   To solve, enter 35 ⟦+⟧ 8 ⟦%⟧   [Answer: $37.80]

2. **Subtracting a Percent from a Number**
   An item is priced at $35.00. If it is discounted at 25%, what is the new sale price of the item?

   To solve, enter 35 ⟦−⟧ 25 ⟦%⟧   [Answer: $26.25]

3. **Multiplying a Number by a Percent**
   An item is priced at $35.00. If the sales tax is 8%, what is the amount of the sales tax?

   To solve, enter 35 ⟦x⟧ 8 ⟦%⟧   [Answer: $2.80]

4. **Dividing a Number by a Percent**
   An item is sale-priced at $35.00. If this sale price is 70% of the original price, what was the original price?

   To solve, enter 35 ⟦÷⟧ 70 ⟦%⟧   [Answer: $50.00]

The student worksheets on pages 31 through 38 provide students practice in working a variety of problems with percent. You may wish to have them practice estimating answers before using their calculators.

Percent

Find the total cost of a pair of shoes that cost $63.95 plus 8% tax.

Press % 63 · 95 + 8 % _____

(Remember: Do not press the = key.)

Use your calculator to find the sum of the number and the percent of that number as indicated. Write a key sequence to show your work. Record your answers on the lines.

1. 75 and 10%

Key sequence % _____ Answer _____

2. 150 and 7%

Key sequence % _____ Answer _____

3. 1,700 and 12%

Key sequence % _____ Answer _____

4. 8,000 and 5.5%

Key sequence % _____ Answer _____

5. 10,750 and 9%

Key sequence % _____ Answer _____

Summer Job

This summer, David took a job in the university bookstore. One of his duties was to determine the selling price of each item sold in the bookstore. Following is a list of markups. All books are marked up 40% over the bookstore's cost of the book, clothing is marked up 20% over cost, and all school supplies are marked up 30% over cost. Use your calculator to help David determine the selling price for each of the items. The bookstore's cost for each item is in the parentheses. (Round the answers to the nearest penny.)

1. math textbook ($14.50 each)

   selling price _____

2. pens ($0.72 each)

   selling price _____

3. school jacket ($30.45 each)

   selling price _____

4. science textbook ($35.10 each)

   selling price _____

5. notebooks ($11.40 per dozen)

   selling price _____

6. school jogging suit ($75.00 per suit)

   selling price _____

7. school sweatshirt ($18.95 each)

   selling price _____

8. history textbook ($25.25 each)

   selling price _____

Percent $\boxed{-}$

Find the difference of a number and a given percent of that number.

Example: 50 minus 20%

Key sequence: $\boxed{^{ON}/_C}$ 50 $\boxed{-}$ 20 $\boxed{\%}$

Answer ___40___

Use your calculator to find the difference of the given number indicated by the percent of that number as indicated. Write a key sequence to show your work.

1. 80 minus 6%

   Key sequence $\boxed{^{ON}/_C}$ _____ Answer _____

2. 360 minus 35%

   Key sequence $\boxed{^{ON}/_C}$ _____ Answer _____

3. 5,000 minus 18%

   Key sequence $\boxed{^{ON}/_C}$ _____ Answer _____

4. 2,060 minus 25%

   Key sequence $\boxed{^{ON}/_C}$ _____ Answer _____

5. 9,500 minus 16.2%

   Key sequence $\boxed{^{ON}/_C}$ _____ Answer _____

Buying Spree

An expensive clothing store is having a gigantic clearance sale. The chart shows what percent each category will be reduced. Use your calculator to determine the sale cost of each item. Record your answers.

Savings Chart	
Coats	20% off
Pants	25% off
Dresses	15% off
Jackets	18% off
Shirts	22% off

1. One jacket originally priced at $95

   Sale price _____

2. Two dresses originally $120 each

   Sale price (each) _____

   Total spent _____

3. One shirt originally priced at $32

   Sale price _____

4. 1 coat originally $480 and 1 coat originally $249.95

   Sale price (1) _____   (2) _____   Total spent _____

5. 3 pairs of pants originally $70 each, 3 jackets originally $120 each,
   4 shirts originally $40 each, and 2 coats originally $220 each

   Pants, sale price _____   Jackets, sale price _____

   Shirts, sale price _____   Coats, sale price _____

   Total spent _____

Name _____ Date _____

Percent ☒

Find the percent of a number.
Record your answer.

Example: Find 9% of $50.00

Key sequence: [ON/C] 50 [×] 9 [%]
Answer __$4.50__

Use your calculator to find the percent of a number. Write a key sequence to show your work. Record your answer.

1. 12% of 300

   Key sequence _____ Answer _____

2. 3% of 90

   Key sequence _____ Answer _____

3. 85% of 25

   Key sequence _____ Answer _____

4. 150% of 12

   Key sequence _____ Answer _____

5. 39% of 39

   Key sequence _____ Answer _____

A Taxing Time

Maria's summer job was in the billing department of a large mail-order house. Her job was to determine the amount of tax an order should be assessed and separately record the tax. Use your calculator to help Maria determine the correct amount of tax for each order based on the tax rate for that state. The number in parentheses indicates the tax rate. Record your answer. (Remember, when necessary, round your answer to the nearest penny.)

1. $16.75 (8%)

   tax _____

2. $20 (7%)

   tax _____

3. $156.25 (11%)

   tax _____

4. $88.95 (7%)

   tax _____

5. $117.40 (6%)

   tax _____

6. $73 (6.5%)

   tax _____

7. $329.63 (7.5%)

   tax _____

8. $950 (5%)

   tax _____

9. $950 (8%)

   tax _____

Percent $\div$

Find the whole number when only a part of the number is known.

Example: 25 is 20% of what number?

Key sequence: [ON/%] 25 $\div$ 20 [%]
answer __125__

Use your calculator to find the whole number when only a part of the number is known. Write a key sequence to show your work. Record your answer in the space provided.

1. 18 is 30% of what number?

   Key sequence [ON/%] _____ Answer _____

2. 39 is 12% of what number?

   Key sequence [ON/%] _____ Answer _____

3. 25 is 20% of what number?

   Key sequence [ON/%] _____ Answer _____

4. 60 is 120% of what number?

   Key sequence [ON/%] _____ Answer _____

5. 130 is 8% of what number?

   Key sequence [ON/%] _____ Answer _____

Being Nosy

Marcia looked at the sales price on some shoes that had been reduced. She wondered what the original selling prices had been. Use your calculator to help Marcia determine the original selling price of these sale shoes. Record your answer. Remember, if necessary, round your answer to the nearest penny.

1. Sale price of $20 is 50% of the original selling price
   original price _____

2. Sale price of $70 is 30% of original selling price
   original price _____

3. Sale price of $145.50 is 75% of original selling price
   original price _____

4. Sale price of $95.99 is 55% of original selling price
   original price _____

5. Sale price of $ 55.50 is 62% of original selling price
   original price _____

6. Sale price of $15 is 18% of original selling price
   original price _____

Teaching Notes

Exploring the Solutions to Word Problems

A calculator may be used in many different ways to work with word problems. It makes it possible for students to explore the solutions to simple word problems in novel ways. Here is one example.

> John wants to buy six apples. Each apple costs 25 cents. What will be the total cost of the apples?

The generally accepted paper-and-pencil way to solve this problem would be to multiply 6 by 25 cents. Or, for younger students, to add 25 cents 6 times.

But, look at these ways of exploring the same problem with a calculator.

1. This way is similar to paper-and-pencil.

   .25 [×] 6 [=]

2. Here the relationship between multiplication and addition is reinforced.

   .25 [+] .25 [+] .25 [+] .25 [+] .25 [+] .25

3. In this method, the use of the addition constant gives a tactile approach. The six presses of the equals key can be thought of as the six addends.

   [+] .25 [=][=][=][=][=][=]

The student worksheets on pages 40 through 42 provide students opportunities to solve word problems in different ways.

Teaching Notes

Finding the Remainder in a Division Problem

When you divide two numbers on a calculator, the quotient is given in decimal form. Here are two ways to find what whole number remainder the decimal part of the answer represents.

Method 1: Here we are reversing the method used to check division. We multiply the whole number part of the answer (5) by the divisor (4) and then subtract that product (20) from the dividend (23) to find the remainder.

Step 1: 23 ÷ 4 =   [Display: 5.75]
Step 2: 5 x 4 =   [Display: 20]
Step 3: 23 − 20 =   [Display: 3]

Method 2: This method uses the fact that multiplying the remainder in decimal form (0.75) by the divisor (4) gives the remainder written as a whole number.

Step 1: 23 ÷ 4 =   [Display: 5.75]
Step 2: 5.75 − 5 =   [Display: 0.75]
Step 3: 0.75 x 4 =   [Answer: 3]

Point out that the three forms of expressing the quotient are equivalent: 5, R 3; 5.75; and $5\frac{3}{4}$ all mean the same thing.

The student worksheets on pages 45 through 47 provide students practice in finding whole-number remainders.

Remainder?

Use your calculator and Method 1 to find the quotient and remainder for the following problem.

38 ÷ 7 = _____ R _____

Press ⌐ON/C⌐ 38 ÷ 7 =   (Display: 5.4285714)   Step 1
      5 ⨯ 7 =   (Display: 35)   Step 2
      38 − 35 =   (Display: 3)   Step 3
      so 38 ÷ 7 = 5 R 3

Use your calculator to find the quotient and the remainder for the following.

1. 69 ÷ 4 = _____ R _____

2. 70 ÷ 9 = _____ R _____

3. 147 ÷ 6 = _____ R _____

4. 904 ÷ 3 = _____ R _____

5. 329 ÷ 13 = _____ R _____

6. 2345 ÷ 28 = _____ R _____

7. 4793 ÷ 197 = _____ R _____

8. 16,682 ÷ 109 = _____ R _____

Remainders Again?

Use your calculator to find the quotient and remainder for the following problem using Method 2.

38 ÷ 7 = _____ R _____

Press ⌷%⌷ 38 ÷ 7 = (Display: 5.4285714)

Press – 5 = (Display: 0.4285714)

Press × 7 (Divisor) = (Display 2.9999998)

2.9999998 rounded to the nearest whole number is __3__.

Therefore, the quotient is __5__ and the remainder is __3__.

Find the quotient and the remainder using Method 2.

1. 48 ÷ 9 = _____ R _____

2. 79 ÷ 6 = _____ R _____

3. 35 ÷ 3 = _____ R _____

4. 219 ÷ 14 = _____ R _____

5. 655 ÷ 17 = _____ R _____

6. 1607 ÷ 10 = _____ R _____

7. 7349 ÷ 100 = _____ R _____

8. 25,094 ÷ 1,000 = _____ R _____

Finding Remainders

Using your calculator, find the quotient and the remainder. Record your results.

Problem	Calculator Answer	Quotient and Remainder
1. 27 ÷ 6		_____ R _____
2. 57 ÷ 8		_____ R _____
3. 58 ÷ 5		_____ R _____
4. 95 ÷ 4		_____ R _____
5. 437 ÷ 5		_____ R _____
6. 123 ÷ 3		_____ R _____
7. 541 ÷ 3		_____ R _____
8. 631 ÷ 6		_____ R _____
9. 78 ÷ 7		_____ R _____
10. 511 ÷ 9		_____ R _____

Teaching Notes

Division by Zero—The Error Message

As you demonstrate with your overhead calculator, have students follow along. Enter 6 $\div$ 0 $=$. What appears on the display? [Answer: The letter E to the left, and a zero to the right.]

The letter E stands for "Error." It means you have asked the calculator to do something that is mathematically impossible, or something that the calculator is not designed to do.

Division by zero is mathematically impossible. Why is it so? Remind students that division and multiplication are inverse operations. This is one of the basic rules of arithmetic. For example, if 6 $\div$ 0 were to equal some number N, then it must be true that N x 0 = 6. Since there is no number N that we can multiply by 0 to get 6, N x 6 = 0 is an equation with no solution, and so is the equation 6 $\div$ 0 = N.

For students with some knowledge of algebra, you might use the following explanation. For any number A, A $\div$ 0 = C would mean that 0 x C = A. If A $\neq$ 0, no value of C can make the last equation a true statement, since 0 x C = 0 for each true value of C. But if A = 0, every value of C makes the equation a true statement. Therefore a quotient of A $\div$ 0 either would have no value or would have an infinite set of values.

The student worksheet on page 49 provides students with an opportunity to explore what happens when you try to divide by zero on the calculator. You may wish to have students do the worksheet first and then discuss the results. Another way to get the E for "Error" is to try taking the square root of a negative number.

48

Danger, Danger!

1. Solve: 8 ÷ 0 =

    Record your answer on the
    line. _____

2. Press 9 [x] 3 [=] _____

    What happened?_____

Your calculator is locked and no calculations can be performed until the incorrect entry
has been cleared.

3. Now press [ON/C]

    What happened?_____

4. See if you can compute 9 [x] 3 [=] _____

Teaching Notes

Estimation and Addition

As you demonstrate with your overhead calculator, have students follow along. Where could you place plus signs to make the following a number sentence? Your students can use estimation and calculators to solve the problem. Is there only one solution?

1 8 1 8 1 8 1 8 1 8 = 1035

Two possible answers are:

18 + 18 + 181 + 818 = 1035
181 + 818 + 18 + 18 = 1035

Have students try their estimation skills by doing these examples along with you. Encourage them to give an estimate that would have the correct number of digits.

Where could you place plus signs to make the following number sentences?

1. 1 2 3 4 5 6 7 8 9 = 963
2. 7 7 7 7 7 7 7 7 7 = 1645

Possible answers:
1. 123 + 45 + 6 + 789 = 963
2. 7 + 7 + 77 + 777 + 777 = 1645

The student worksheet on page 51 provides students practice in using estimation to arrange numbers that add to a given sum.

50

Think! (Estimate and Check)

Example: Place only "+" signs between the digits to build numbers that enable you to arrive at the given answers. Use your estimation skills and your calculator to check your work.

1   2   3   4   5   6 = 174

123 + 45 + 6 = 174

Press [ON/C]

123 [+] 45 [+] 6 = 174

Place only "+" signs between the digits to build numbers that enable you to arrive at the given answer.

1. 1   4   2   8   9   5   1   6 = 36

2. 2   4   6   3   5   2   1   9   1   7 = 175

3. 3   3   4   4   2   2   5   5   6   6   7   7 = 1,989

4. 4   5   7   8   6   2   8   4 = 10,862

5. 5   2   0   4   3   1   8   2 = 538

6. 1   1   1   1   1   1   1   1   1   1 = 1,234

Teaching Notes

Estimation and Multiplication

As you demonstrate with your overhead calculator, have students follow along with the worksheet on the next page. Find the largest possible product using the digits 1, 2, 3, 4, and 5 only once each in the boxes below.

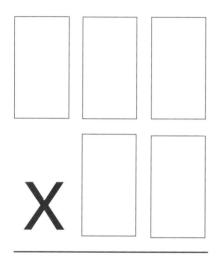

Begin by asking the students which digit should be in the hundreds place. [Answer: One of the larger numbers, either 4 or 5, should be in the hundreds place.] Then have them use trial and error to position the other four digits. [Answer: The largest possible product is 431 x 52 = 22,412.]

Students can use the same method to find the smallest possible product. [Answer: The smallest possible product is 245 x 13 = 3185.] Begin by asking which digit should be in the hundreds place. [Answer: One of the smaller numbers, either 1 or 2, should be in the hundreds place.]

The student worksheet on page 53 provides students practice in using estimation to find products of whole numbers.

Play Time

Using each number only once, arrange the digits 1, 2, 3, 4, and 5 in the boxes below so that you get the largest possible product.

Largest Product _____

Smallest Product _____

Change the digits to 5, 6, 7, 8, and 9. Now find the:

Largest Product _____

Smallest Product _____

53

Teaching Notes

Introducing the Concept of Ratio

As you demonstrate with your overhead calculator, have students follow along. Make the number 0.01 appear on the display without using the decimal point key. Answers might be recorded in a chart like the following.

First No.	Divided By	Second No.	Equals 0.01

Have students try to do this problem in several ways. Write all the student answers on the overhead.

Possible answers:

$$1 \div 100 = 0.01$$
$$2 \div 200 = 0.01$$
$$9 \div 900 = 0.01$$
$$10 \div 1,000 = 0.01$$
$$30 \div 3,000 = 0.01$$
$$88 \div 8,800 = 0.01$$

Ask the students what the relationship is between the numbers used. [Answer: Since the result (quotient) 0.01 is the same, the division of each of the two numbers is also the same. The ratio between the two numbers in each answer is 1 to 100. This ratio can also be written as a fraction.]

The student worksheet on page 55 provides students practice in the concept of ratio.

Making a Point

Write two different key sequences that will display each of the following numbers.

1. 0.1

2. 0.2

3. 0.03

4. 0.25

5. 1.5

6. 2.3

You cannot use the ● or the % key.

1.   0.1

_____

_____

2.   0.2

_____

_____

3.   0.03

_____

_____

4.   0.25

_____

_____

5.   1.5

_____

_____

6.   2.3

_____

_____

Teaching Notes

Using the Calculator to Count

As you demonstrate with your overhead calculator, have students follow along.

To count by ones, enter $+$ 1 $=$ $=$ $=$ . . .

To count by twos, enter $+$ 2 $=$ $=$ $=$ . . .

To count by fives, enter $+$ 5 $=$ $=$ $=$ . . .

Have students try all counting problems by doing these examples along with you.

1. Make the calculator count by fours.
[Answer: $+$ 4 $=$ $=$ $=$ . . .]

2. Make the calculator count by elevens.
[Answer: $+$ 11 $=$ $=$ $=$ . . .]

3. Make the students count by twelves.
[Answer: $+$ 12 $=$ $=$ $=$ . . .]

4. Make the students count by twenties.
[Answer: $+$ 20 $=$ $=$ $=$ . . .]

5. Make the calculator count by fifties.
[Answer: $+$ 50 $=$ $=$ $=$ . . .]

The student worksheets on pages 57 and 58 provide students practice in using the calculator to count.

Count-A-Rama

Example: Make your calculator count by sixes to 42.

Write the key sequence to show how you did it.

Key sequence: [ON/C] [+] 6 [=] [=] [=] [=] [=] [=] [=] _____

Make the calculator count. Write the key sequence to show your work. Remember to press [ON/C] before beginning each new problem.

1. Count by 4s to 20.
   Key sequence _____

2. Count by 9s to 72.
   Key sequence _____

3. Count by 10s to 100.
   Key sequence _____

4. Count by 1000s to 15,000.
   Key sequence _____

   _____

5. Count by 100,000 to one million.
   Key sequence _____

   _____

   _____

AmaR-A-tnuoC (Count-A-Rama, Backwards)

Example: Make your calculator count backwards from 80 to zero by 10s. Write a key sequence to show your work.

Press ⌑ 80 − 10 = = = = = = = =

Make your calculator count backwards as indicated. Write a key sequence to show your work.

1. Count from 40 to 16 by 4s.

   _____

2. Count from 200 to 75 by 25s.

   _____

3. Count from 750 to 50 by 100s.

   _____

4. Count from 51 to 9 by 7s.

   _____

5. Count from 321 to 71 by 50s.

   _____

Noting New Numbers—The Negative

Example: Make your calculator count backwards from 15 by threes to zero. Note the new numbers. Continue counting backwards by pressing ⬚= five more times. What number is on the display now? Write a key sequence to show your work.

Press ⬚ON/C 15 ⬚− 3 ⬚= ⬚= ⬚= ⬚= ⬚= ___0___
⬚= ⬚= ⬚= ⬚= ⬚= ___−15___

Make your calculator count backwards to zero from the number indicated, then press ⬚= four more times. What number is on the display? Write a key sequence to show your work.

1. Count from 25 by 5s _____

2. Count from 18 by 6s _____

3. Count from 63 by 9s _____

4. Count from 72 by 12s _____

5. Count from 75 by 15s _____

Using Addition and Subtraction of Integers

On pages 55 and 56, your students learned how to count forward by adding positive integers. On pages 58 and 59, they learned how to count backwards by subtracting positive integers. We can also count forward by subtracting negative integers and count backwards by adding negative integers.

As you demonstrate with your overhead calculator, have students follow along.

Count forward from 0 by subtracting negative numbers:

To subtract –1s, enter 1 $\boxed{+/_-}$ $\boxed{-}$ $\boxed{=}$ $\boxed{=}$ $\boxed{=}$. . .

To subtract –2s, enter 2 $\boxed{+/_-}$ $\boxed{-}$ $\boxed{=}$ $\boxed{=}$ $\boxed{=}$. . .

Have students try counting forward from 0 by subtracting –3s, then –5s, then –8s.

Count backwards from 0 by adding negative numbers:

To add –1s, enter 1 $\boxed{+/_-}$ $\boxed{+}$ $\boxed{=}$ $\boxed{=}$ $\boxed{=}$. . .

To add –2s, enter 2 $\boxed{+/_-}$ $\boxed{+}$ $\boxed{=}$ $\boxed{=}$ $\boxed{=}$. . .

Have students try counting backwards from 0 by adding –3s, –4s, and –50s.

The student worksheets on pages 63 and 64 provide students practice in counting forwards and backwards with integers.

Counting Is Counting, Right?

Make your calculator count forward by subtracting a negative number.

Example: Count forward from 25 to 40 by subtracting –5s.

Press	Display
ON/C	0
25	25
–	25
5	5
+/–	–5
=	30
=	35
=	40

Make your calculator count forward by subtracting a negative. Show your work.

1. Count forward from 1 to 6 by –1.

Press	Display
ON/C	0

2. Count forward from 2 to 12 by –2.

Press	Display
ON/C	0

3. Count forward from 18 to 42 by –4.

Press	Display
ON/C	0

4. Count forward from –9 to 12 by –3s.

Press	Display
ON/C	0

5. Count forward from –24 to 24 by –6s.

Press	Display
ON/C	0

63

More Mixed-Up Math

Make your calculator count backwards by adding a negative number.

Example: Count backwards from
20 to 8 by adding −4.

Press	Display
ON/C	0
20	20
+	20
4	4
+/−	-4
=	16
=	12
=	8

Make your calculator count backwards
by adding a negative number.

1. Count backwards from 10 to 0
   by adding −2.

Press	Display
ON/C	0

2. Count backwards from 40 to 10
   by adding −5.

Press	Display
ON/C	0

3. Count backwards from −24 to −40
   by adding −4.

Press	Display
ON/C	0

4. Count backwards from 0 to −60
   by adding −12.

Press	Display
ON/C	0

Teaching Notes

Skip-counting with Decimals

As you demonstrate with your overhead calculator, have students follow along.

To count by 0.1s, enter $\boxed{+}$ $\boxed{\cdot}$ $\boxed{1}$ $\boxed{=}$ $\boxed{=}$ $\boxed{=}$ . . .
[Answer: 0.1, 0.2, 0.3, 0.4, 0.5, 0.6, and so on.]

To count by 0.5s, enter $\boxed{+}$ $\boxed{\cdot}$ $\boxed{5}$ $\boxed{=}$ $\boxed{=}$ $\boxed{=}$. . .
[Answer: 0.5, 1, 1.5, 2, 2.5, 3, 3.5, and so on.]

To count by 0.25s, enter $\boxed{+}$ $\boxed{\cdot}$ $\boxed{2}$ $\boxed{5}$ $\boxed{=}$ $\boxed{=}$ $\boxed{=}$ . . .
[Answer: 0.25, 0.5, 0.75, 1, 1.25, 1.5, and so on.]

Have students try counting with decimals by doing these examples along with you.

1. Make the calculator count by 0.3s.
   [Answer: 0.3, 0.6, 0.9, 1.2, 1.5, 1.8, and so on.]

2. Make the calculator count by 0.6s.
   [Answer: 0.6, 1.2, 1.8, 2.4, 3, 3.6, and so on.]

3. Make the calculator count by 1.5s.
   [Answer: 1.5, 3, 4.5, 6, 7.5, 9, and so on.]

4. Make the calculator count by 3.25s.
   [Answer: 3.25, 6.5, 9.75, 13, 16.25, 19.5, and so on.]

The student worksheets on pages 66 and 67 provide students practice in counting with decimals.

No Unnecessary Numbers: Counting by Decimals

How does the calculator count by decimals?
Make your calculator count by 0.20 to 1.20.
Record your work on the chart.

Press	Display
ON/C	0.
·	0.
20	0.20
+	0.2
=	0.2
=	0.4
=	0.6
=	0.8
=	1.
=	1.2

Make your calculator count by the decimal
indicated and record your work as you go along.

1. Count by 0.50 to 2.5

Press	Display
ON/C	0

2. Count by 0.75 to 5.25

Press	Display
ON/C	0

3. Count by 0.125 to 1.

Press	Display
ON/C	0

4. Count by 0.08 to 0.8

Press	Display
ON/C	0

Equals! Equals! Equals!

Press	Display
ON/C	0.
·	0.
25	0.25
+	0.25
=	0.25
=	0.5
=	0.75
=	1.
=	1.25

Determine how many times the = must be pressed if you count by 0.25 to 1.25. Show your work. Record your answer.

Determine how many times the = must be used to arrive at the given number. Show your work and record your answer.

1. Count by 0.625 to 5.

Press	Display
ON/C	0.

The number of times you pressed = : _____

2. Count by 4.375 to 35.

Press	Display
ON/C	0.

The number of times you pressed = : _____

Do not show your work on 3 and 4. Write the number of times you pressed = to arrive at the given number.

3. Count by 0.73 to 15.33. = : _____

4. Count by 0.14 to 1.96. = : _____

Teaching Notes

Arithmetic Patterns with Addition

As you demonstrate with your overhead calculator, have the students follow along. Here is how to use the addition constant to make a pattern. Enter: $+$ 2.5 $=$. Then enter 3 $=$ $=$ $=$ and so on. The pattern appearing on the display is 3, 5.5, 8, 10.5, and so on.

How would you describe the pattern? [Answer: The first number is 3, the second number is 2.5 more than the first number, the third number is 2.5 more than the second number, and so on.]

Remind the students that the second number (addend) in an addition problem becomes a constant when $=$ is pressed repeatedly. Each time the $=$ key is pressed, the second addend is added to the current number on the display.

Have students experiment to create these patterns. Once they have found a way to make each pattern, have them record the key sequence.

1. 1, 3, 5, 7, 9   [Answer: $+$ 2 $=$ 1 $=$ $=$ $=$]

2. 3, 7, 11, 15, 19   [Answer: $+$ 4 $=$ 3 $=$ $=$ $=$]

3. 2, 13, 24, 35, 46   [Answer: $+$ 11 $=$ 2 $=$ $=$ $=$]

4. 19, 44, 69, 94, 119   [Answer: $+$ 25 $=$ 19 $=$ $=$ $=$]

5. 1, 1.5, 2, 2.5, 3   [Answer: $+$ 0.5 $=$ 1 $=$ $=$ $=$]

6. 2, 3.5, 5, 6.5, 8   [Answer: $+$ 1.5 $=$ 2 $=$ $=$ $=$]

The student worksheet on page 69 provides students practice in creating arithmetic patterns.

I Calculate, I Create

Create a number pattern using your addition constant. Begin your pattern with 1 and use 3 as your constant. List the first four members of your pattern.

Press	ON/C	+	3	=	1	=	=	=	=
Display	0.	0.	3	3	1	4	7	10	13

Write a key sequence for a number pattern using the addition constant on your calculator. Begin your pattern with 1 and use the number in parentheses as your constant. List the first five members of your pattern.

1. (2)

Press	ON/C							
Display	0.							

2. (6)

Press	ON/C							
Display	0.							

3. (20)

Press	ON/C							
Display	0.							

4. (1.5)

Press	ON/C							
Display	0.							

5. (0.25)

Press	ON/C							
Display	0.							

Game: Find an Addition Pattern

In this game, students use the calculator to find addition patterns.

Materials: calculator, paper, pencil

Number of players: 2–4

Object: Find a secret pattern by recording the numbers appearing in the display window when the $=$ is pressed.

Type of pattern to be entered: In secret, Player 1 enters a pattern into the calculator using the addition constant. (Example: $^{ON}\!/_C$ $+$ 7 $=$ 4)

Rules for Play: Once Player 1 enters a pattern, he hands the calculator to Player 2. Player 2 may press the $=$ one to four times. He should record the numbers displayed after each $=$. Before pressing the $=$ for the fifth time, Player 2 names the next number in the sequence. He then presses the $=$. If his guess is correct, he presses $^{ON}\!/_C$ and reenters the same pattern as Player 1 entered. If he is successful, Player 2 enters a new secret pattern for player 1 to discover. Play continues until each player has had a chance to discover a pattern and enter a pattern for someone else to discover.

Scoring: Player 2 gets five points by identifying a pattern, plus ten points by reproducing the pattern. Player 1 gets fifteen points if Player 2 does not identify or reproduce the pattern entered by Player 1.

Winning the Game: After each player has had a chance to both discover and create a pattern, the player with the highest point total wins.

Teaching Notes

Arithmetic Patterns with Subtraction

As you demonstrate with your overhead calculator, have the students follow along. Here is how to use the subtraction constant to make a pattern. Enter: $-$ 3 $=$. Then enter 50 $=$ $=$ $=$ and so on. The pattern appearing on the display is 50, 47, 44, 41, and so on.

How would you describe the pattern? [Answer: The first number is 50, the second number is 3 less than the first number, the third number is 3 less than the second number, and so on.]

Remind the students that the second number (subtrahend) in a subtraction problem becomes a constant when the $=$ sign is pressed repeatedly. Each time the $=$ key is pressed, the subtrahend is subtracted from the current number on the display.

Have students experiment to create these patterns. Once they have found a way to make each pattern, have them record the key sequence.

1. 29, 27, 25, 23, 21   [Answer: $-$ 2 $=$ 29 $=$ $=$ $=$]

2. 42, 37, 32, 27, 22   [Answer: $-$ 5 $=$ 42 $=$ $=$ $=$]

3. 101, 86, 71, 56, 41   [Answer: $-$ 15 $=$ 101 $=$ $=$ $=$]

4. 200, 165, 130, 95, 60   [Answer: $-$ 35 $=$ 200 $=$ $=$ $=$]

5. 10, 9.5, 9, 8.5, 8   [Answer: $-$ .5 $=$ 10 $=$ $=$ $=$]

6. 30, 27.5, 25, 22.5, 20   [Answer: $-$ 2.5 $=$ 30 $=$ $=$ $=$]

The student worksheet on page 72 provides students practice in creating arithmetic patterns.

Don't Take Away My Creation!

Create a number pattern using your subtraction constant. Begin your pattern with the given number and use the number in parentheses as your constant. List the first four members of your pattern.

For 10 (2)

Press	ON/C	−	2	=	10	=	=	=	=
Display	0.	0.	2	-2	10	8	6	4	2

Write a key sequence for a number pattern using the subtraction constant on your calculator. Begin your pattern with the given number and use the number in parentheses as your constant. List the first five members of your pattern.

1. 32 (4)

Press	ON/C								
Display	0.								

2. 57 (7)

Press	ON/C								
Display	0.								

3. 160 (20)

Press	ON/C								
Display	0.								

4. 90 (15)

Press	ON/C								
Display	0.								

5. 18 (2.5)

Press	ON/C								
Display	0.								

Game: Find a Subtraction Pattern

In this game, students use the calculator to find subtraction patterns.

Materials: calculator, paper, pencil

Number of players: 2–4

Object: Find a secret pattern by recording the numbers appearing in the display window when the = is pressed.

Type of pattern to be entered: In secret, Player 1 enters a pattern into the calculator using the subtraction constant. (Example: ON/C – 5 = 4)

Rules for play: Once Player 1 enters a pattern, he hands the calculator to Player 2. Player 2 may press the = one to four times. She should record the numbers displayed after each =. Before pressing the = for the fifth time, Player 2 names the next number in the sequence. She then presses the =. If her guess is correct, she presses ON/C and reenters the same pattern as Player 1 entered. If she is successful, Player 2 enters a new secret pattern for Player 1 to discover. Play continues until each player has had a chance to discover a pattern and enter a pattern for someone else to discover.

Scoring: Player 2 gets five points by identifying a pattern, plus ten points by reproducing the pattern. Player 1 gets fifteen points if Player 2 does not discover the pattern Player 1 entered.

Winning the game: After each player has had a chance to both discover and create a pattern, the player with the highest point total wins.

Teaching Notes

Geometric Patterns with Multiplication

As you demonstrate with your overhead calculator, have students follow along. Here is how to use the multiplication constant to make a pattern. Enter: 2 ☒ ═ . Then enter 5 ═ ═ ═ and so on. The pattern appearing on the display is 5, 10, 20, 40.

How would you describe the pattern? [Answer: The first number is 5, the second number is 2 times the first number, the third number is 2 times the second number, and so on. This is a geometric pattern.]

Remind students that the first number (factor) in a multiplication problem becomes a constant when the ═ is pressed repeatedly. Each time the ═ is pressed, the first factor is multiplied by the current number on the display.

Have students find the key sequences for these patterns.

1. 3, 6, 12, 24, 48   [Answer: 2 ☒ 3 ═ ═ ═]

2. 2, 6, 18, 54, 162   [Answer: 3 ☒ 2 ═ ═ ═]

3. 2, 10, 50, 250, 1250   [Answer: 5 ☒ 2 ═ ═ ═]

4. 5, 15, 45, 135, 405   [Answer: 3 ☒ 5 ═ ═ ═]

5. 20, 10, 5, 2.5, 1.25   [Answer: .5 ☒ 20 ═ ═ ═]

6. 24, 36, 54, 81, 121.5   [Answer: 1.5 ☒ 24 ═ ═ ═]

The student worksheet on page 75 provides students practice in creating geometric patterns.

Multiplying a Creation

Create a number pattern using your multiplication constant. Begin your pattern with 1 and use the number in parentheses as your constant. List the first five members of your pattern.

Press	ON/C	4	x	=	1	=	=	=	=
Display	0.	4	4	16	1	4	16	64	256

Write a key sequence for a number pattern using the multiplication constant on your calculator. Begin your pattern with 1 and use the number in parentheses as your constant. List the first five members of your pattern.

1. (2)

Press	ON/C							
Display	0.							

2. (3)

Press	ON/C							
Display	0.							

3. (10)

Press	ON/C							
Display	0.							

4. (1.5)

Press	ON/C							
Display	0.							

5. (20)

Press	ON/C							
Display	0.							

Teaching Notes

Game: Find a Multiplication Pattern

In this game, students use the calculator to find multiplication patterns.

Materials: calculator, paper, pencil

Number of players: 2–4

Object: Find a secret pattern by recording the numbers appearing in the display window when the $=$ is pressed.

Type of pattern to be entered: In secret, Player 1 enters a pattern into the calculator using the multiplication constant. (Example: $\boxed{\frac{ON}{C}}$ 4 $\boxed{x}$ $\boxed{=}$ 5)

Rules for play: Once Player 1 enters a pattern, he hands the calculator to Player 2. Player 2 may press the $\boxed{=}$ one to four times. He should record the numbers displayed after each $\boxed{=}$. Before pressing the $\boxed{=}$ for the fifth time, Player 2 names the next number in the sequence. He then presses the $\boxed{=}$. If his guess is correct, he presses $\boxed{\frac{ON}{C}}$ and reenters the same pattern as Player 1 entered. If he is successful, Player 2 enters a new secret pattern for Player 1 to discover. Play continues until each player has had a chance to discover a pattern and enter a pattern for someone else to discover.

Scoring: Player 2 gets five points by identifying a pattern, plus ten points by reproducing the pattern. Player 1 gets fifteen points if Player 2 does not discover the pattern Player 1 entered.

Winning the game: After each player has had a chance to both discover and create a pattern, the player with the highest point total wins.

Teaching Notes

Geometric Patterns with Division

As you demonstrate with your overhead calculator, have students follow along. Here is how to use the division constant to make a pattern. Enter: $\div$ 2 $=$. Then enter 96 $=$ $=$ $=$ and so on. The pattern appearing on the display is 96, 48, 24, 12.

How would you describe the pattern? [Answer: The first number is 96, the second number is one half the first number, the third number is one half the second number, and so on. This is a geometric pattern.]

Remind students that the second number (divisor) in a division problem becomes a constant when the $=$ is pressed repeatedly. Each time the $=$ is pressed, the current number on the display is divided by the original divisor.

Have students try to create patterns by doing these examples along with you.

1. 162, 54, 18, 6, 2   [Answer: $\div$ 3 $=$ 162 $=$ $=$ $=$]

2. 6250, 1250, 250, 50   [Answer: $\div$ 5 $=$ 6250 $=$ $=$ $=$]

3. 1, 0.2, 0.04, 0.008, 0.0016   [Answer: $\div$ 5 $=$ 1 $=$ $=$ $=$]

4. 216, 360, 600, 1000   [Answer: $\div$ 0.6 $=$ 216 $=$ $=$ $=$]

5. 0.1, 0.05, 0.025, 0.0125   [Answer: $\div$ 2 $=$ 0.1 $=$ $=$ $=$]

6. 0.999, 0.333, 0.111, 0.037   [Answer: $\div$ 3 $=$ 0.999 $=$ $=$ $=$]

The student worksheet on page 78 provides students practice in creating patterns in division.

Creating Patterns in Division

Create a division number pattern using your
division constant.

Press	ON/C	÷	3	=	243	=	=	=	=
Display	0.	0.	3	0	243	81	27	9	3

Write a key sequence for a number pattern using the division constant on your
calculator. Begin your pattern with 1 and use the number parentheses as your
constant. List the first five members of your pattern.

1. 64 (2)

Press	ON/C							
Display	0.							

2. 7776 (6)

Press	ON/C							
Display	0.							

3. 4000 (20)

Press	ON/C							
Display	0.							

4. 20 (0.2)

Press	ON/C							
Display	0.							

5. 78,125 (5)

Press	ON/C							
Display	0.							

Game: Find a Division Pattern

In this game, students use the calculator to find division patterns.

Materials: calculator, paper, pencil

Number of players: 2–4

Object: Find a secret pattern by recording the numbers appearing in the display window when the $=$ is pressed.

Type of pattern to be entered: In secret, Player 1 enters a pattern into the calculator using the division constant. (Example: ON/C $\div$ 2 $=$ 800)

Rules for play: Once Player 1 enters a pattern, he hands the calculator to Player 2. Player 2 may press the $=$ one to four times. He should record the numbers displayed after each $=$. Before pressing the $=$ for the fifth time, Player 2 names the next number in the sequence. He then presses the $=$. If his guess is correct, he presses ON/C and reenters the same pattern as Player 1 entered. If he is successful, Player 2 enters a new secret pattern for Player 1 to discover. Play continues until each player has had a chance to discover a pattern and enter a pattern for someone else to discover.

Scoring: Player 2 gets five points by identifying a pattern, plus ten points by reproducing the pattern. Player 1 gets fifteen points if Player 2 does not discover the pattern Player 1 entered.

Winning the game: After each player has had a chance to both discover and create a pattern, the player with the highest point total wins.

Teaching Notes

Game: Guess a Rule

In this game, students use the calculator to find rules.

Materials: calculator, paper, pencil

Number of players: 2

Rules for play: Using addition or subtraction, Player 1 enters a secret operation and a constant, such as "Subtract 2." Then Player 1 chooses a secret beginning number such as 20.

Press	ON/C	20	−	2	=
Display	0.	20	20	2	18

Player 1 hands the calculator showing 18 on the display to Player 2. To guess the secret rule, Player 2 presses any number followed by = three times.

Press	3	=	4	=	5	=
Display	3	1	4	2	5	3

Encourage Player 2 to think of the three entered numbers in this more simplified way.

Press	3	4	5
Display	1	2	3

Player 2 guesses the rule "Subtract 2."

Scoring: Player 2 gets five points for a correct answer. Player 2 then tries to reenter the same rule. If successful, Player 2 gets ten more points. If Player 2 is not successful, Player 1 gets fifteen points. Play continues until both players have had a turn creating and guessing a rule.

The student worksheet on page 81 may be used to play this game.

Guess A Rule

1. Press _____

   Display | | |

   Rule _____

2. Press _____

   Display | | |

   Rule _____

3. Press _____

   Display | | |

   Rule _____

4. Press _____

   Display | | |

   Rule _____

5. Press _____

   Display | | |

   Rule _____

6. Press _____

   Display | | |

   Rule _____

Teaching Notes

Using the Identity Property to Guess a Rule

If your students have not already found a quick way to discover the rule in the game Guess a Rule on pages 78 and 79, then you may want to represent the mathematics involved.

Your students know that ANY NUMBER + 0 = THAT NUMBER (N + 0 = N). This statement is called the Identity Property of Addition. The identity element for addition is 0.

So, in the example for Guess a Rule, if your students had first tried 0, they would have found the constant, -2, on the display.

Press	ON/C	20	−	2	=	0	=
Display	0	20	20	2	18	0	–2

Extension: You know that ANY NUMBER x 1 = THAT NUMBER (N x 1 = N). This statement is called Identity Property of Multiplication. The identity element for multiplication is 1.

Have your students try a problem with a constant factor.

Enter 3 x 8 =, so that 3 is the constant factor.

Press	ON/C	3	x	8	=
Display	0.	3	3	8	24

Ask what number should be entered to solve the rule quickly. [Answer: Entering 1 = displays 3, the constant factor, on the display.] What happens if 0 is entered? [Answer: Entering 0 = displays 0, since any number x 0 = 0.]

Teaching Notes

Fraction and Decimal Equivalents

As you demonstrate with your overhead calculator, have students follow along. What are the decimal equivalents of $\frac{1}{4}$, $\frac{2}{4}$, $\frac{3}{4}$, $\frac{4}{4}$, $\frac{5}{4}$, and so on? Have your students use the division constant, since each fraction above is a numerator divided by 4.

$$1 \boxed{\div} 4 \boxed{=} \quad \text{[Answer: 0.25]}$$

$$2 \boxed{=} \quad \text{[Answer: 0.5]}$$

$$3 \boxed{=} \quad \text{[Answer: 0.75]}$$

$$4 \boxed{=} \quad \text{[Answer: 1]}$$

$$5 \boxed{=} \quad \text{[Answer: 1.25]}$$

Now have your students find the decimal equivalents of the following fractions using the denominator as the division constant.

1. $\frac{1}{6}$, $\frac{2}{6}$, $\frac{3}{6}$, $\frac{4}{6}$, $\frac{5}{6}$
   [Answers: 0.1666, 0.333, 0.5, 0.666, 0.8333]

2. $\frac{1}{9}$, $\frac{2}{9}$, $\frac{3}{9}$, $\frac{4}{9}$, $\frac{5}{9}$
   [Answers: 0.111, 0.222, 0.333, 0.444, 0.555]

3. $\frac{1}{50}$, $\frac{2}{50}$, $\frac{3}{50}$, $\frac{4}{50}$, $\frac{5}{50}$
   [Answers: 0.02, 0.04, 0.06, 0.08, 0.1]

4. $\frac{1}{12}$, $\frac{2}{12}$, $\frac{3}{12}$, $\frac{4}{12}$, $\frac{5}{12}$
   [Answers: 0.08333, 0.1666, 0.25, 0.333, 0.41666]

The student worksheets on pages 84 through 89 provide students practice in using the division constant.

Changing Fractions to Decimals

Example: Use the division constant to find decimals for $\frac{1}{4}, \frac{2}{4}, \frac{3}{4}, \frac{4}{4}$.

Press	ON/C	1	÷	4	=	2	=	3	=	4	=
Display	0	1	1	4	0.25	2	0.5	3	0.75	4	1

Look for a pattern. Use the division constant.

1. $\frac{1}{5}$ =

2. $\frac{2}{5}$ =

3. $\frac{3}{5}$ =

4. $\frac{4}{5}$ =

5. $\frac{5}{5}$ =

6. $\frac{6}{5}$ =

7. $\frac{7}{5}$ =

8. $\frac{8}{5}$ =

9. $\frac{9}{5}$ =

10. $\frac{10}{5}$ =

11. $\frac{1}{8}$ =

12. $\frac{2}{8}$ =

13. $\frac{3}{8}$ =

14. $\frac{4}{8}$ =

15. $\frac{5}{8}$ =

16. $\frac{6}{8}$ =

17. $\frac{7}{8}$ =

18. $\frac{8}{8}$ =

19. $\frac{9}{8}$ =

20. $\frac{10}{8}$ =

What pattern do you see in problems 1–10? _____

_____

What pattern do you see in problems 11–20? _____

_____

Changing Fractions to Decimals (continued)

Look for a pattern. Use the division constant.

1. $\frac{1}{10}$ =

2. $\frac{2}{10}$ =

3. $\frac{3}{10}$ =

4. $\frac{4}{10}$ =

5. $\frac{5}{10}$ =

6. $\frac{6}{10}$ =

7. $\frac{7}{10}$ =

8. $\frac{8}{10}$ =

9. $\frac{9}{10}$ =

10. $\frac{10}{10}$ =

11. $\frac{1}{20}$ =

12. $\frac{2}{20}$ =

13. $\frac{3}{20}$ =

14. $\frac{4}{20}$ =

15. $\frac{5}{20}$ =

16. $\frac{6}{20}$ =

17. $\frac{7}{20}$ =

18. $\frac{8}{20}$ =

19. $\frac{9}{20}$ =

20. $\frac{10}{20}$ =

21. $\frac{11}{20}$ =

22. $\frac{12}{20}$ =

23. $\frac{13}{20}$ =

24. $\frac{14}{20}$ =

25. $\frac{15}{20}$ =

26. $\frac{16}{20}$ =

27. $\frac{17}{20}$ =

28. $\frac{18}{20}$ =

29. $\frac{19}{20}$ =

30. $\frac{20}{20}$ =

What pattern do you see? _____

_____

Teaching Notes

Estimating Square Roots

As you demonstrate with your overhead calculator, have students follow along with the worksheet on page 91. Your calculator already finds a square root of a number with a special key: $\boxed{\sqrt{}}$. But what if there were no $\boxed{\sqrt{}}$ on your calculator? Could you still find the square roots of numbers? Have your students use approximation and the multiplication constant to find $\sqrt{30}$.

Between what two perfect squares is 30?
[Answer: 25 = 5 x 5 and 36 = 6 x 6.]

A reasonable starting point might be 5.5.
Enter: 5.5 $\boxed{\times}$ $\boxed{=}$ [Display: 30.25]

Good guess, but 30.25 is just a little too large.
So let's try   5.4 $\boxed{\times}$ $\boxed{=}$ [Display: 29.16]

29.16 is too small and is farther away from 30 than 30.25.
So let's try 5.47 $\boxed{\times}$ $\boxed{=}$ [Display: 29.9209]

29.9209 is too small.
So let's try 5.48 $\boxed{\times}$ $\boxed{=}$ [Display: 30.0304]

Very close, but 30.0304 is just a little too large.

We can continue this estimation process until we find a value of $\sqrt{30}$ to the limits of the calculator, 5.4772255.

Now estimate the square roots of 5, 40, and 200.
[Answers: 2.2360679, 6.3245553, and 14.142135]

92

Estimating Square Root

Record each try. Estimate $\sqrt{30}$.

	Guess	x =
1st		
2nd		
3rd		
4th		
5th		
6th		
7th		
8th		
9th		
10th		

Game: Estimating Decimal Sums

In this game, students use the calculator to check their estimated answers.

Materials: calculator

Number of players: Any number may play.

Rules for play: Give students addition problems with decimal numbers and missing addends. For example, 5 + ___ = 8.6. Each player gets five seconds and one try to guess the missing addend in a given addition problem and enter it on his calculator display. (The number may also be entered in the memory so that it may be verified later.)

Two players may not guess the same addend. (The order of the players should alternate each round so that each player has a chance to be first, second, etc.)

After all players have made their guesses, they should each complete the problem on their calculators and read their answers aloud.

Scoring: The player guessing the addend that results in a sum equal to or closest to but less than the given sum wins the round and is awarded ten points.

Winning the game: The first player to reach 100 points wins the game.

The student worksheet on page 95 may be used to play this game.

The Addition Estimation Game (Decimals)

Problem	Player A Score	Player B Score	Player C Score

Game: Estimating Decimal Products

In this game, students use the calculator to check their estimated answers.

Materials: calculator

Number of players: Any number may play.

Rules for play: Give students multiplication problems with decimal numbers and missing factors. For example, 2 x ___ = 10.4. Each player gets five seconds and one try to guess the missing factor in a given multiplication problem and enter it on his calculator display. (The number may also be entered in the memory so that it may be verified later.)

Two players may not guess the same factor. (The order of the players should alternate each round so that each player has a chance to be first, second, etc.)

After all players have made their guesses, they should each complete the problem on their calculators and read their answers aloud.

Scoring: The player guessing the factor that results in a product equal to or closest to but less than the given product wins the round and is awarded ten points.

Winning the game: The first player to reach 100 points wins the game.

The student worksheet on page 97 may be used to play this game.

The Multiplication Estimation Game (Decimals)

Problem	Player A Score	Player B Score	Player C Score

Game: Guess the Fraction

In this game, students use the calculator to find fractional equivalents of the number 1.

Materials: calculator

Number of players: 2

Rules for play: Using the division constant, Player 1 enters a quotient equal to 1, such as 321 $\div$ 321 $=$. Then Player 1 hands the calculator showing 1 on the display to Player 2.

To guess the fraction equal to 1, Player 2 presses any number followed by $=$. Player 2 continues until the correct fraction is found.

Scoring: Player 2 gets ten points for a correct answer on the first try. For each additional try that is needed, 1 fewer point is awarded. Play continues with players 1 and 2 alternating turns.

Winning the game: The player with the greatest number of points wins the game.

The student worksheet on page 99 may be used to play this game.

Finding the Fraction Equivalent of 1

	Score	
Player A		**Player B**

1. _____   _____

2. _____   _____

3. _____   _____

4. _____   _____

5. _____   _____

6. _____   _____

7. _____   _____

8. _____   _____

9. _____   _____

10. _____   _____

Finding the Limit of a Process

What happens when you multiply a number by itself repeatedly? Or when you press the square root key over and over? It depends on the kind of number!

As you demonstrate with the overhead calculator, have students follow along. Have them look for patterns in the answers.

Repeated Multiplication

16 [x] [=] [=] [=] and so on.
[Answer: The sixth [=] produces an E for overloaded.]

0.5 [x] [=] [=] [=] and so on.
[Answer: Pressing the [=] key twenty–three times gives 0.]

Multiplying a number greater than 1 repeatedly eventually produces an overload. If the number is less than 1, you will eventually get 0.

Repeated Square Root

16 [√] [√] [√] and so on.
[Answer: Pressing the [√] key twenty-four times gives 1.]

0.5 [√] [√] [√] and so on.
[Answer: Pressing the [√] key twenty-three times gives 1.]

Repeatedly pressing the square root key will eventually result in the number 1 or a number very close to 1 such as 0.9999997.

For example, pressing 0.4 [√] and so on produces many numbers in the display that begin with 0.9999999.

The student worksheet on page 101 provides students an opportunity to find the limits of processes.

How Far Can You Go?

Multiply

1. 24 $\boxed{\times}$ $\boxed{=}$ $\boxed{=}$ . . .

   How many times did you press $\boxed{=}$ before E appeared on the display? _____

2. 0.2 $\boxed{\times}$ $\boxed{=}$ $\boxed{=}$ . . .

   What happened? _____

   How many times did you press $\boxed{=}$ before that happened? _____

Square Root

3. 81 $\boxed{\sqrt{}}$ $\boxed{\sqrt{}}$ . . .

   What happened? _____

   How many times did you press $\boxed{\sqrt{}}$ before that happened? _____

4. 0.36 $\boxed{\sqrt{}}$ $\boxed{\sqrt{}}$ . . .

   What happened? _____

   How many times did you press $\boxed{\sqrt{}}$ before that happened? _____

Teaching Notes

Rounding Calculator Answers

The calculator truncates or shortens numbers. It does not round them up. To demonstrate this, enter 2 ÷ 3 on your overhead calculator. [The display reads 0.6666666.] Ask students if the answer is rounded. [Answer: No, a rounded answer would be 0.6666667.]

Occasionally, this feature of a calculator means that you must make adjustments in answers. As you demonstrate with your overhead calculator, have students follow along.

2 ÷ 3 =   [Display: 0.6666666]

x 3 =   [Display: 1.9999998]

Have students find (2 ÷ 3) x 3 without using a calculator. [Answer: 2] Explain that when dividing with certain numbers such as 3, 6, and 9, the calculator is giving an approximate answer.

Would it help if the calculator rounded answers up? To show what happened, enter the following. Point out that the answer is still not exact. It must be rounded to 2.

0.6666667 x 3 = [Display: 2.0000001]

The student worksheet on page 103 provides students practice in deciding when to round calculator answers.

Rounding

Convert each fraction to a decimal. Tell which answers are exact, which are shortened, and which you would need to round.

1. $\frac{1}{3}$ = _____

2. $\frac{1}{6}$ = _____

3. $\frac{3}{8}$ = _____

4. $\frac{5}{12}$ = _____

5. $\frac{3}{11}$ = _____

6. $\frac{7}{15}$ = _____

7. $\frac{2}{3}$ x 3 = _____

8. $\frac{5}{12}$ x 12 = _____

9. $\frac{3}{11}$ x 11 = _____

10. $\frac{7}{15}$ x 15 = _____

Teaching Notes

Adding and Subtracting Fractions

All answers on the calculator are in decimal form. This activity changes the decimal part of an answer to its fraction equivalent.

For example, let's change the decimal part of 2.75 to a fraction. We need a whole number by which we can multiply the decimal to give us another whole number. One possibility is 4, where 0.75 x 4 = 3. This means that 0.75 equals the fraction $\frac{3}{4}$, where 4 becomes the denominator and 3 is the numerator. So, 2.75 equals the mixed number $2\frac{3}{4}$.

Use this problem to demonstrate with your overhead calculator. Have students follow along.

$$\frac{4}{5} + \frac{3}{4} = (4 \div 5) + (3 \div 4)$$

Enter: 4 $\boxed{\div}$ 5 $\boxed{=}$ $\boxed{\text{M+}}$ 3 $\boxed{\div}$ 4 $\boxed{=}$ $\boxed{\text{M+}}$ $\boxed{\text{M}^{\text{R}}_{\text{C}}}$

The answer is 1.55. To change 0.55 to a fraction, multiply it by both the denominators in the original problem. Pressing 0.55 $\boxed{\text{x}}$ 5 $\boxed{\text{x}}$ 4 $\boxed{=}$ gives 11. The numerator is 11.

The denominator equals the product of the denominators: (4 x 5), or 20.
So, 1.55 $=$ $1\frac{11}{20}$.

The student worksheet on page 105 provides students practice in converting decimal answers to fraction equivalents.

Can You Add and Subtract Fractions?

Use your calculator. Change each decimal answer to a fraction in simplest form.

Example: $\frac{3}{5}$ + $\frac{3}{4}$

Press ⏻ 3 ÷ 5 = M+

3 ÷ 4 = M+ M꜀ᴿ ___1.35___

.35 × 5 × 4 = ___7___

The denominator is 20, so 1.35 = $1\frac{7}{20}$.

Add

1. $\frac{1}{2}$ + $\frac{3}{4}$ =

2. $\frac{1}{8}$ + $\frac{4}{5}$ =

3. $\frac{1}{4}$ + $\frac{3}{5}$ =

4. $\frac{1}{2}$ + $\frac{1}{3}$ =

5. $\frac{2}{5}$ + $\frac{3}{4}$ =

6. $\frac{1}{6}$ + $\frac{1}{2}$ =

7. $\frac{1}{9}$ + $\frac{1}{3}$ =

8. $\frac{2}{3}$ + $\frac{4}{5}$ =

Subtract

9. $\frac{3}{4}$ − $\frac{1}{2}$ =

10. $\frac{4}{5}$ − $\frac{1}{8}$ =

11. $\frac{3}{5}$ − $\frac{1}{4}$ =

12. $\frac{1}{2}$ − $\frac{1}{3}$ =

13. $\frac{3}{4}$ − $\frac{2}{5}$ =

14. $\frac{1}{2}$ − $\frac{1}{6}$ =

15. $\frac{1}{3}$ − $\frac{1}{9}$ =

16. $\frac{4}{5}$ − $\frac{2}{3}$ =

Display the Number

Students can use the calculator to display given numbers in the least number of keystrokes. This activity uses trial and error as well as estimation.

Here are three examples for you to present with your overhead calculator. Have students follow along.

Number to Display	Digits	Keys to be Used
5	2	Any
340	3, 7	Any
9	2	+ ÷ =

To display 5 using all 2s, you might think of 5 as equal to 1 plus 4. Then, one possible sequence is 2 ÷ 2 + 2 = = . Written as a number sentence, this would be $(2 \div 2) + 2 + 2 = 5$.

To display 340 using just 3s and 7s, a hint is that $7 \times 7 \times 7 = 343$. Then, $343 - 3 = 340$. One answer is 7 × = = − 3 = . As a number sentence, this is $(7 \times 7 \times 7) - 3 = 340$.

To display 9 using 2s and just the + , ÷ , and = keys, again remember that $2 \div 2 = 1$. As a number sentence, one answer is $(2 \div 2) + 2 + 2 + 2 + 2 = 9$. The key sequence is 2 ÷ 2 + 2 = = = = .

The student worksheet on page 107 may be used for this activity.

106

Display the Number

Display each number in the first column by using only the keys given in that row. Use the fewest number of keystrokes. Then describe each process as a number sentence.

For rows 9 – 12, make up your own problems.

	Number to be Displayed	Digits	Keys to be Used (Operations or Functions)	Number Sentence
1.	5	2	any	
2.	98	7	any	
3.	340	3, 7	any	
4.	84	7	any	
5.	1000	8	any	
6.	2200	1, 3	any	
7.	9	2	$+$, $\div$, $=$	
8.	11	2	$+$, $\cdot$, $=$	
9.				
10.				
11.				
12.				

Teaching Notes

Converting Units of Measure

The constant feature on the calculator can be used to convert feet to inches, ounces to pounds, millimeters to meters, and so on. As you demonstrate with your overhead calculator, have students follow along.

To complete the table below, set 12 as a multiplication constant. The first problem will be entered 12 $\boxed{\times}$ 2 $\boxed{=}$. For the rest of the table, enter the number of feet followed by $\boxed{=}$.

Feet	2	5	8	10	12	15	20
Inches							

To complete this table, set 1000 as constant. The first problem would be entered as 9 $\boxed{\div}$ 1000 $\boxed{=}$.

Millimeters	9000	7500	4850	1275	520	65	2
Meters							

Remind students that the first number is the constant in a multiplication problem. In a division problem, it is the second number that is the constant.

The student worksheet on page 109 provides students practice in using the constant feature to convert units of measure.

Making Conversion Tables

Follow the directions of your teacher. Complete the tables using the <u>constant</u> feature of your calculator.

1.

2.

3.

Teaching Notes

Writing Number Sentences

Students here will use all four operations to reach given numbers. Trial and error is an important part of this activity.

Place 35 on the display. In one step (operation), display 100. Here are three possible answers.

35 + 65 =	35 + 65 = 100
35 − 65 +/− =	35 − (−65) = 100
35 ÷ 0.35 =	35 ÷ 0.35 = 100

Place 35 on the display. In two steps, display 100. Here are two possible answers.

35 x 3 =	35 x 3 = 105
105 − 5 =	105 − 5 = 100
35 ÷ 0.7 =	35 ÷ 0.7 = 50
50 x 2 =	50 x 2 = 100

Place 35 on the display. In three steps, display 100. One answer is shown.

35 x 4 =	35 x 4 = 140
140 + 10 =	140 + 10 = 150
150 − 50 =	150 − 50 = 100

The student worksheet on page 111 provides students practice in writing number sentences as they experiment to find given numbers.

110

Writing Number Sentences

1. Place a number under N. Set your goal. Choose one operation (+, −, x, ÷) and enter a number ? that will give you your goal.

Example:

N	operation	?	goal
42	x	3	126

2. Place a number under N. Set your goal. Choose two steps and record your answers.

Example:

N	operation	?	operation	?	goal
45	+	5	x	2	100

Teaching Notes

Estimating Cube Roots

Your calculator does not have a special key to find the cube root of a number. But, you can use approximation to find cube roots. Remind students that finding the cube root of 125, for example, is the same as solving the problem N x N x N = 125.

As you demonstrate with your overhead calculator, have students follow along.

Between what two perfect cubes is 80?
[Answer: 64 = 4 x 4 x 4 and 125 = 5 x 5 x 5]

A reasonable starting point might be 4.4.
Enter: 4.4 $\boxed{\text{x}}$ $\boxed{=}$ $\boxed{=}$ [Display: 85.184]

Good guess, but 85.184 is too large.
So let's try 4.3 $\boxed{\text{x}}$ $\boxed{=}$ $\boxed{=}$ [Display: 79.507]

79.507 is too small but is closer to 80 than 85.184.
So let's try, 4.31 $\boxed{\text{x}}$ $\boxed{=}$ $\boxed{=}$ [Display: 80.062991]

80.062991 is just a little too large.
So let's try 4.305 $\boxed{\text{x}}$ $\boxed{=}$ $\boxed{=}$ [Display: 79.784672]

Very close, but 79.784672 is too small.

We can continue this estimation process until we find a value to the limits of the calculator, 4.3088694.

Remember that the calculator does not round off its answers. The cube root of a number that is not perfect can only be approximated.

Now estimate the cube roots of 10, 50, and 100.
[Answers: 2.1544346, 3.6840314, and 4.6415888.]

112

Teaching Notes

The Largest Products

Any calculator has a limited capacity. If you try to multiply numbers that are too large, you will get an error message to show that you have exceeded the capacity of the calculator.

As you demonstrate with your overhead calculator, have students follow along. Enter 79,856 $\boxed{\times}$ 85,324 $\boxed{=}$. What does the display show? [Answer: E68.136333] Remind students that they must clear the calculator before starting a new problem.

Have students estimate this product by finding 80,000 x 85,324. To find the estimate, multiply 8 times 85,324 on the calculator. Then add four zeros to the answer on the display. [Answer: 6,825,920,000] Could you get a closer estimate? [Answer: Yes, 799 x 85,324 = 68,173,876. And, 68,173,876 x 100 = 6,817,387,600.]

How many digits can be shown on the display? [Answer: 8] What is the largest number on the display? [Answer: 99,999,999] Find pairs of whole numbers you can multiply to get 99,999,999. [Possible answers: 9 and 11,111,111; 99 and 1,010,101]

What is the largest number with a decimal part that can be shown on the calculator? [Answer: 9,999,999.9] find parts of decimals you can multiply to get this product. [Possible answers: 9 and 1,111,111.1; 99 and 101,010.1]

The student worksheet on page 114 gives students an opportunity to find pairs of numbers that result in large products.

Experimenting with Large Products

1. Find the largest product using whole numbers. Record your attempts here.

A	x	B	Answer

2. Find the largest product using decimals. Record your attempts here.

A	x	B	Answer

Teaching Notes

Beyond the Calculator—Addition

By using the associative property, you can add numbers that are too large for the display of the calculator. You can also find sums where the answer will be too large.

Have students follow along as you demonstrate with your overhead calculator. To add 555,666,777,888 to 222,333,444,999, think of breaking each number into two parts.

555,666,777,888 = 555,666,000,000 + 777,888

222,333,444,999 = 222,333,000,000 + 444,999

Now you can work the problem in two parts.

Part 1   777,888 + 444,999 =   [Display: 1,222,887]

Part 2   555,666 + 222,333 + 1 =   [Display: 778,000]

Notice in Part 2 that 1 million is added to the millions. Why? The answer is formed by writing the millions in front of the last six digits of Part 1. The answer is 778,000,222,887.

Here are some problems for your students to try.

1. 777,555,333,111 + 888,666,444,222
2. 806,883,902,176 + 944,367,192,873
3. 5,496,789,011,339 + 917,395,687,529 + 45,788,668,304
4. $46,768,239.98 + $9,552,964.86
5. $75,920,559.65 + $459,288,546.90 + $1,590,456.88

Beyond the Calculator—Subtraction

You can also subtract numbers that are too large for the display of the calculator and find differences where the answer will be too large.

Have students follow along as you demonstrate with your overhead calculator. To find 888,666,222,555 minus 444,111,777,999, think of breaking each number in two parts.

888,666,222,555 = 888,660,000,000 + 6,222,555

444,111,777,999 = 444,110,000,000 + 1,777,999

Now you can work the problem in two parts.

Part 1   6,222,555 − 1,777,999 =   [Display: 4,444,556]

Part 2   88,866 − 44,411 =   [Display:44,455]

The answer is formed by writing 44,455 in front of the last seven digits of Part 1. The answer is 444,554,444,556.

Here are some problems for your students to try.

1.   999,555,333,111 − 888,666,444,222

2.   816,888,972,106 − 640,364,152,863

3.   6,475,789,471,529 − 35,898,658,354

4. $48,755,249.99 − $7,382,945.86

5. $165,927,544.15 − $66,268,536.50

Teaching Notes

Beyond the Calculator—Multiplication

You can multiply numbers that are too large for the display of the calculator or where the answer will be too large for the display by using the distributive property. To find 77,888,555 times 44,999, think of breaking each number in two parts.

77,888,555 = 77,888,000 + 555

44,999 = 44,000 + 999

Now set up the problem like this, finding each of the four partial products.

	A		B	
	77,888		555	

		C	D
X		44	999

```
                554,445    (B x D)
            77,810,112     (A x D)
                24,420     (B x C)
         3,427,072         (A x C)
      ─────────────────
      3,504,907,086,445
```

Note: The number of digits in each partial product should not exceed eight. This will ensure that each product will fit on the display.

Here are some problems for your students to try.

1. 55,333,777 x 444,222
2. 832,196 x 7,152,803

Answers

Page 5   **1.** 5   **2.** 4   **3.** 9   **4.** 5   **5.** 2   **6.** 7   **7.** 8   **8.** 7   **9.** 5   **10.** 7

Page 6   **1.** 2   **2.** 4   **3.** 1   **4.** 0   **5.** 1   **6.** 5   **7.** 3   **8.** 2   **9.** 4   **10.** 3

Page 7   **1.** 105   **2.** 95   **3.** 500   **4.** 20   **5.** 21   **6.** 51   **7.** 68   **8.** 4
   9. 20   **10.** 14   **11.** 84   **12.** 8   **13.** 6   **14.** 70   **15.** 90   **16.** 84

Page 8   **1.** 401 tons   **2.** 323,945 square feet   **3.** 16 feet   **4.** 44 feet

Page 10   **1.** 13   **2.** 11   **3.** 18   **4.** 25   **5.** 33

Page 12   **1.** 54   **2.** 120   **3.** 0   **4.** 29   **5.** 47   **6.** 21   **7.** 14   **8.** 27

Page 13   **1.** 60   **2.** 63   **3.** 92   **4.** 50   **5.** 35   **6.** 42   **7.** 39   **8.** 40   **9.** 63

Page 15   **1.** 3, 6, 9, 12   **2.** 7, 14, 21, 28   **3.** 15, 20, 25, 30   **4.** 75, 100, 125, 150
   5. 10, 12, 14, 16   **6.** 13, 16, 19, 22

Page 16   **1.** 7, 32, 59, 155, 100   **2.** 45, 115, 320, 30, 21   **3.** $21.00
   4. $7.39   **5.** $125.55   **6.** $101.59

Page 18   **1.** 20, 16, 12, 8   **2.** 80, 70, 60, 50   **3.** 175, 150, 125, 100   **4.** 72, 63, 54, 45
   5. 50, 45, 40, 35

Page 19   **1.** 39, 77, 164, 392, 1   **2.** 16, 5, 49, 155, 0
   3. $12.17, $45.29, $139.79, $9.70, $135.58

Page 21   **1.** 25, 125, 625   **2.** 3,600; 216,000; 12,960,000   **3.** 9, 27, 81   **4.** 100; 1,000; 10,000
   5. 2,500; 125,000; 6,250,000   **6.** 400; 8,000; 160,000

Page 22   **1.** 70, 135, 400; 1,000   **2.** 12, 177, 273, 450   **3.** 748, 493, 289,102, 204, 510, 340

Page 24   **1.** 124, 62, 31   **2.** 125, 25, 5   **3.** 250, 62.5, 15.625   **4.** 243, 81, 27
   5. 100,000; 10,000; 1,000

Page 25   **1.** 9, 23, 224, 17   **2.** 187, 16, 125, 27

Page 27   **1.** −5   **2.** 6   **3.** 40   **4.** 70   **5.** −75   **6.** 31   **7.** 98   **8.** −124
   9. 7,432   **10.** −3,675

Page 29   **1.** 4   **2.** 12   **3.** 8   **4.** 25   **5.** 7.6157731   **6.** 81   **7.** 10.954451
   8. 4.0199502   **9.** 5.0487622

Page 31   **1.** 75 + 10%; 82.5   **2.** 150 + 7%; 160.5   **3.** 1,700 + 12%; 1,904
   4. 8,000 + 5.5%; 8,440   **5.** 10,750 + 9%; 11,717.5

Page 32   **1.** $20.30   **2.** $0.94   **3.** $36.54   **4.** $49.14   **5.** $14.82
   6. $90.00   **7.** $22.74   **8.** $35.35

Page 33   **1.** 80 − 6%; 75.2   **2.** 360 − 35%; 234   **3.** 5,000 − 18%; 4,100
   4. 2,060 − 25%; 1,545   **5.** 9,500 − 16.2%; 7,961

Page 34 1. $77.90 2. $102, $204 3. $24.96 4. $384, $199.96, $583.96
5. $157.50, $295.20. $124.80, $352.00, $929.50

Page 35 1. 300 x 12%; 36 2. 90 x 3%; 2.7 3. 25 x 85%; 21.25
4. 12 x 150%; 18 5. 39 x 39%; 15.21

Page 36 1. $1.34 2. $1.40 3. $17.19 4. $6.23 5. $7.04 6. $4.75
7. $24.72 8. $47.50 9. $76

Page 37 1. 18 ÷ 30%; 60 2. 39 ÷ 12%; 325 3. 25 ÷ 20%; 125
4. 60 ÷ 120%; 50 5. 130 ÷ 8%; 1,625

Page 38 1. $50 2. $233.33 3. $194.00 4. $174.53 5. $89.52
6. $83.33

Page 40 The total cost of the apples is $1.50. In explaining how the three methods are related, student answers will vary. A sample answer is given. In Method A, 0.25 is multiplied by 6. In Method B, 0.25 is added to itself 6 times. This gives the same answer as multiplying by 6. In Method C, the addition constant on the calculator is used. When the equals key is pressed six times, you have added 0.25 to itself six times. This is the same mathematical method as in Method B, but you get the answer more quickly.

Page 41 1. 112 cups 2. 30.48 cm 3. $9.90 4. 136 minutes 5. 15,924 pounds

Page 42 Maria can buy six apples. In explaining how the three methods are related, student answers will vary. A sample answer is given. In Method A, $1.50 is divided by 25 cents to give six apples. In Method B, you start with $1.50 and then subtract 25 cents until you have no money left. As you subtract, you count the number of times you get six. Method C is similar to Method B, except that you use the subtraction constant. In Method D, you add 25 cents each time until you get $1.50 and count the number of times you add the 25 cents. Method E is similar to Method D but uses the addition constant. In Method F, you find multiples of 25 cents until you hit $1.50.

Page 43 1. 9 gallons 2. 5 kilograms 3. 8 pounds 4. 25 miles

Page 45 1. 17, R1 2. 7, R7 3. 24, R3 4. 301, R1 5. 25, R4 6. 83, R21
7. 24, R65 8. 153, R5

Page 46 1. 5, R3 2. 13, R1 3. 11, R2 4. 15, R9 5. 38, R9 6. 160, R7
7. 73, R49 8. 25, R94

Page 47 1. 4.5; 4, R3 2. 7.125; 7, R1 3. 11.6; 11, R3 4. 23.75; 23, R3 5. 87.4; 87, R2
6. 41; 41, R0 7. 180.33333; 180, R1 8. 105.16666; 105, R1
9. 11.142857; 11, R1 10. 56.777777; 56, R7

Page 49 1. E, 0 2. Nothing. The calculator is locked. 3. The calculator is cleared.
4. Yes, the answer is 27.

Page 51 Answers may vary. Samples are given.
1. 1 + 4 + 2 + 8 + 9 + 5 + 1 + 6 = 36
2. 24 + 63 + 52 + 19 + 17 = 175 3. 334 + 442 + 556 + 677 = 1,989
4. 4,578 + 6,284 = 10,862 5. 520 + 4 + 3 + 1 + 8 + 2 = 538
6. 1,111 + 111 + 11 + 1 = 1,234

119

Page 53   For the digits 1 through 5, the largest product is 431 x 52 = 22,412. The smallest product is 245 x 13 = 3,185. For the digits 5 through 9, the largest product is 875 x 96 = 84,000. The smallest is 689 x 57 = 39,273.

Page 55   Answers will vary.

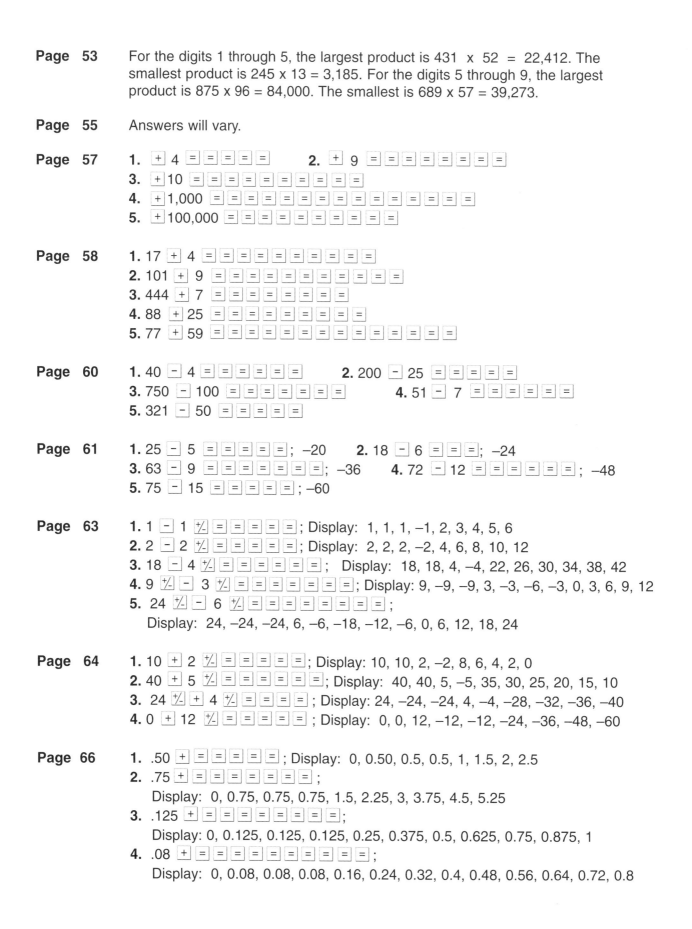

Page 57   **1.** [+] 4 [=][=][=][=][=]   **2.** [+] 9 [=][=][=][=][=][=][=]
3. [+] 10 [=][=][=][=][=][=][=][=][=]
4. [+] 1,000 [=][=][=][=][=][=][=][=][=][=][=][=][=]
5. [+] 100,000 [=][=][=][=][=][=][=][=][=][=]

Page 58   **1.** 17 [+] 4 [=][=][=][=][=][=][=][=][=][=]
2. 101 [+] 9 [=][=][=][=][=][=][=][=][=][=][=]
3. 444 [+] 7 [=][=][=][=][=][=][=]
4. 88 [+] 25 [=][=][=][=][=][=][=][=]
5. 77 [+] 59 [=][=][=][=][=][=][=][=][=][=][=][=][=]

Page 60   **1.** 40 [−] 4 [=][=][=][=][=][=]   **2.** 200 [−] 25 [=][=][=][=][=]
3. 750 [−] 100 [=][=][=][=][=][=][=]   **4.** 51 [−] 7 [=][=][=][=][=][=][=]
5. 321 [−] 50 [=][=][=][=][=][=]

Page 61   **1.** 25 [−] 5 [=][=][=][=][=]; −20   **2.** 18 [−] 6 [=][=][=]; −24
3. 63 [−] 9 [=][=][=][=][=][=][=]; −36   **4.** 72 [−] 12 [=][=][=][=][=][=][=]; −48
5. 75 [−] 15 [=][=][=][=][=]; −60

Page 63   **1.** 1 [−] 1 [+/−][=][=][=][=][=]; Display: 1, 1, 1, −1, 2, 3, 4, 5, 6
2. 2 [−] 2 [+/−][=][=][=][=][=]; Display: 2, 2, 2, −2, 4, 6, 8, 10, 12
3. 18 [−] 4 [+/−][=][=][=][=][=][=]; Display: 18, 18, 4, −4, 22, 26, 30, 34, 38, 42
4. 9 [+/−] [−] 3 [+/−][=][=][=][=][=][=][=]; Display: 9, −9, −9, 3, −3, −6, −3, 0, 3, 6, 9, 12
5. 24 [+/−] [−] 6 [+/−][=][=][=][=][=][=][=][=];
Display: 24, −24, −24, 6, −6, −18, −12, −6, 0, 6, 12, 18, 24

Page 64   **1.** 10 [+] 2 [+/−][=][=][=][=][=]; Display: 10, 10, 2, −2, 8, 6, 4, 2, 0
2. 40 [+] 5 [+/−][=][=][=][=][=][=][=]; Display: 40, 40, 5, −5, 35, 30, 25, 20, 15, 10
3. 24 [+/−] [+] 4 [+/−][=][=][=][=]; Display: 24, −24, −24, 4, −4, −28, −32, −36, −40
4. 0 [+] 12 [+/−][=][=][=][=][=]; Display: 0, 0, 12, −12, −12, −24, −36, −48, −60

Page 66   **1.** .50 [+] [=][=][=][=][=][=]; Display: 0, 0.50, 0.5, 0.5, 1, 1.5, 2, 2.5
2. .75 [+] [=][=][=][=][=][=][=];
Display: 0, 0.75, 0.75, 0.75, 1.5, 2.25, 3, 3.75, 4.5, 5.25
3. .125 [+] [=][=][=][=][=][=][=][=];
Display: 0, 0.125, 0.125, 0.125, 0.25, 0.375, 0.5, 0.625, 0.75, 0.875, 1
4. .08 [+] [=][=][=][=][=][=][=][=][=][=];
Display: 0, 0.08, 0.08, 0.08, 0.16, 0.24, 0.32, 0.4, 0.48, 0.56, 0.64, 0.72, 0.8

120

Page 67

1. .625 [+] [=] [=] [=] [=] [=] [=] [=] [=] ; Display: 0, 0.625, 0.625, 0.625, 1.25, 1.875, 2.5, 3.125, 3.75, 4.375, 5; The equals key is pressed 8 times.

2. 4.375 [+] [=] [=] [=] [=] [=] [=] [=] [=]; Display: 4.375, 4.375, 4.375, 8.75, 13.125, 17.5, 21.875, 26.25, 30.625, 35; The equals key is pressed 8 times.

3. 21 times   4. 14 times

Page 69

1. [+] 2 [=] 1 [=] [=] [=] [=] ; Display: 0, 2, 2, 1, 3, 5, 7, 9

2. [+] 6 [=] 1 [=] [=] [=] [=] ; Display: 0, 6, 6, 1, 7, 13, 19, 25

3. [+] 20 [=] 1 [=] [=] [=] [=] ; Display: 0, 20, 20, 1, 21, 41, 61, 81

4. [+] 1.5 [=] 1 [=] [=] [=] [=] ; Display: 0, 1.5, 1.5, 1, 2.5, 4, 5.5, 7

5. [+] .25 [=] 1 [=] [=] [=] [=] ; Display: 0, 0.25, 0.25, 1, 1.25, 1.5, 1.75, 2

Page 72

1. [−] 4 [=] 32 [=] [=] [=] [=] ; Display: 0, 4, −4, 32, 28, 24, 20, 16

2. [−] 7 [=] 57 [=] [=] [=] [=] ; Display: 0, 7, −7, 57, 50, 43, 36, 29

3. [−] 20 [=] 160 [=] [=] [=] [=]; Display: 0, 20, −20, 160, 140, 120, 100, 80

4. [−] 15 [=] 90 [=] [=] [=] [=] ; Display: 0, 15, −15, 90, 75, 60, 45, 30

5. [−] 2.5 [=] 18 [=] [=] [=] [=] ; Display: 0, 2.5, −2.5, 18, 15.5, 13, 10.5, 8

Page 75

1. 2 [×] [=] 1 [=] [=] [=] [=]; Display: 2, 2, 4, 1, 2, 4, 8, 16

2. 3 [×] [=] 1 [=] [=] [=] [=]; Display: 3, 3, 9, 1, 3, 9, 27, 81

3. 10 [×] [=] 1 [=] [=] [=] [=]; Display: 10; 10; 100; 1; 10; 100; 1,000; 10,000

4. 1.5 [×] [=] 1 [=] [=] [=] [=]; Display: 1.5, 1.5, 2.25, 1, 1.5, 2.25, 3.375, 5.0625

5. 20 [×] [=] 1 [=] [=] [=] [=]; Display: 20; 20; 400; 1; 20; 400; 8,000; 160,000

Page 78

1. [÷] 2 [=] 64 [=] [=] [=] [=] ; Display: 0, 2, 0, 64, 32, 16, 8, 4

2. [÷] 6 [=] 7,776 [=] [=] [=] [=] ; Display: 0; 6; 0; 7,776; 1,296; 216; 36; 6

3. [÷] 20 [=] 4,000 [=] [=] [=] [=] ; Display: 0; 20; 0; 4,000; 200; 10; 0.5; 00.25

4. [÷] 0.2 [=] 20 [=] [=] [=] [=] ; Display: 0; 0.2; 0; 20; 100; 500; 2,500; 12,500

5. [÷] 5 [=] 78,125 [=] [=] [=] [=]; Display: 0; 5; 0; 78,125; 15,625; 3,125; 625; 125

Page 84

1. 0.2   2. 0.4   3. 0.6   4. 0.8   5. 1   6. 1.2   7. 1.4   8. 1.6
9. 1.8   10. 2.0   11. 0.125   12. 0.25   13. 0.375   14. 0.5
15. 0.625   16. 0.75   17. 0.875   18. 1   19. 1.125   20. 1.25

In problems 1 to 10, the pattern is that the answers increase by 0.2. In problems 11 to 20, the answers increase by 0.125.

Page 85

1. 0.1   2. 0.2   3. 0.3   4. 0.4   5. 0.5   6. 0.6   7. 0.7
8. 0.8   9. 0.9   10. 1   11. 0.05   12. 0.1   13. 0.15
14. 0.2   15. 0.25   16. 0.3   17. 0.35   18. 0.4   19. 0.45
20. 0.5   21. 0.55   22. 0.6   23. 0.65   24. 0.7   25. 0.75
26. 0.8   27. 0.85   28. 0.9   29. 0.95   30. 1

In problems 1 to 10, the pattern is that the answers increase by 0.1.
In problems 11 to 30, the pattern is that the answers increase by 0.05.

Page 86

1. 0.5   2. 0.5   3. 0.5   4. 0.5   5. 0.5   6. 0.375   7. 0.375
8. 0.375   9. 0.375   10. 0.375   11. 0.5833   12. 0.5833
13. 0.5833   14. 0.5833   15. 0.5833   16. 0.6667
17. 0.6667   18. 0.6667   19. 0.6667   20. 0.6667

The pattern is that the answers for each group of five problems are the same.

121

Page 87   1. 0.111…   2. 0.222…   3. 0.333…   4. 0.444…   5. 0.555…
6. 0.666…   7. 0.777…   8. 0.888…   9. 1   10. 1.111…
11. 1.222…   12. 1.333…   13. 1.444…   14. 1.555…   15. 1.666…
16. 1.777…   17. 1.888…   18. 2   19. 2.111…   20. 2.222…
All the answers are repeating decimals. The repeating digit increases by
1 each time.

Page 88   1. 0.1428571   2. 0.2857142   3. 0.4285714   4. 0.5714285
5. 0.7142857   6. 0.8571428   7. 1   8. 1.1428571
9. 1.2857142   10. 1.4285714
The pattern is that the answers increase by 0.1428571.

Page 89   1. 0.1428571 + 0.2857142 + 0.4285714 + 0.5714285 + 0.7142857;
Answers will vary; 2.1428569   2. 0.4285714 − 0.1428571 − 0.2857142;
Answers will vary; 0.0000001

Page 91   1. 50%   2. 25%   3. 40%   4. 70%   5. 62.5%   6. 14%
7. 12.5%   8. 33.3%   9. 22.2%   10. 16.67%
(Answers to problems 8, 9, and 10 are rounded.)

Page 101   1. 5 times   2. After pressing the equals key 10 times, you get zero.
3. After pressing the square root key 25 times, you get 1.
4. After pressing the square root key 24 times, you get 0.9999998.

Page 103   1. 0.3333333   2. 0.1666666   3. 0.375   4. 0.4166666
5. 0.2727272   6. 0.4666666   7. 2   8. 5   9. 3   10. 7

Page 105   1. $1\frac{1}{4}$ 2. $\frac{37}{40}$ 3. $\frac{17}{20}$ 4. $\frac{5}{6}$ 5. $1\frac{3}{20}$ 6. $\frac{2}{3}$
7. $\frac{4}{9}$ 8. $1\frac{7}{15}$ 9. $\frac{1}{4}$ 10. $\frac{27}{40}$ 11. $\frac{7}{20}$ 12. $\frac{1}{6}$
13. $\frac{7}{20}$ 14. $\frac{1}{3}$ 15. $\frac{2}{9}$ 16. $\frac{2}{15}$

Page 107   Answers will vary. Sample answers are given.
1. (2 ÷ 2) + 2 + 2 = 5   2. (7 x 7) + (7 x 7) = 98
3. (7 x 7 x 7) − 3 = 340   4. 77 + 7 = 84
5. 888 + (8 x 8) + (8 x 8) − 8 − 8 = 1,000
6. 3,333 − 1,111 − (33 − 11) = 2,200
7. (2 ÷ 2) + 2 + 2 + 2 + 2 = 9
8. 2.2 + 2.2 + 2.2 + 2.2 + 2.2 = 11

Page 114   Answers will vary. Sample answers are given.
1. 9 x 11,111,111 = 99,999,999
2. 9 x 1,111,111.1 = 9,999,999.9

Index